MAX and MORITZ in English dialects and creoles

WILHELM BUSCH

MAX AND MORITZ

in English dialects
and creoles

edited by

Manfred Görlach

HELMUT BUSKE VERLAG HAMBURG

The full texts of five translations and excerts
from another eight are available on
a set of two 90″ cassettes
ISBN 3-87118-702-x

CIP-Kurztitelaufnahme der Deutschen Bibliothek

Max and Moritz, in Engl. dialects and creoles
Wilhelm Busch. Ed. by Manfred Görlach.
Hamburg: Buske, 1986.
NE: Görlach, Manfred [Hrsg.]

ISBN 3-87118-701-1
© HELMUT BUSKE VERLAG HAMBURG 1986

Printed by Bücherdruckkunst, Hamburg

CONTENTS

PREFACE

A special feature of the present collection is that it contains, between the covers of one book, the largest sample, in a numerical as well as geographical sense, of English dialect and creole translations of the same complete text. What is more, all the versions were written for the present book (commissioned by the editor, apart from the two that he wrote himself), and all are gems in themselves – the only danger being that there will not be many readers in the world who can do justice to, or enjoy, all of them, and that the multiplicity here offered in parallel may dim the achievement of the individual translator. This collection is an obvious sister volume to *Max und Moritz in deutschen Dialekten, Mittelhochdeutsch und Jiddisch* (Hamburg: Buske, 1982) in which I gathered an even greater number of existing and newly commissioned versions of the story, with an introduction to German dialects, and a full bibliography of some 130 translations known to me at that time.

Since dialects must be listened to as well as read, the 'German' and the 'English' collection are accompanied by a set of cassettes each; the one accompanying this book contains readings by the authors of L, G, E and J, and selections from N, I, A, S, C, K, T, O and M.

The main objective of the present book is not, of course, a scholarly introduction to varieties of English and English-based pidgins and creoles. It is, rather, to give delight to all those interested in such variation and those who love their own dialect (or that of their grandparents) – even if they do not understand all the finer points.

It is therefore the texts that count in this book, and thanks and admiration are due to my colleagues who joined in the fun and continued their rhyming in the face of other urgent obligations. They have, I hope, never mistaken my promptings or regarded my suggestions as unfair. It is to my fellow translators that I wish to dedicate this book:

J. K. Annand, Roland Bibby, Jean D'Costa, Derick Herning, Freddie Jones, Don Laycock, Derrick McClure, Hans H. Meier, Elly Miller, Stephen Mulrine, A. N. Seymour and – especially – Loreto Todd.

INTRODUCTION

Everyone must think they've had it;
No! they're still alive and at it!

þincstu þæt hie wyrd forspilde?
Giet hie lifaþ, reðe ond wilde!

It is a curious coincidence that Wilhelm Busch and Lewis Carroll were both born in 1832
and that *Max und Moritz* and *Alice in Wonderland* — books that made their authors
unforgettable to the children of their nations (less so, around the world) — were both
published in 1865. And although both Busch and Carroll wrote many books after that,
neither was ever able to repeat the success of the one book that made his name.

Wilhelm Busch was born on April 15, 1832, the eldest son of a shopkeeper at Wiedensahl,
a small village not too far from Hanover. In *Max und Moritz,* he recreated some of his
boyhood adventures at Ebergötzen (near Göttingen, a hundred miles from home), where
he stayed with his uncle, the village parson, for much of his school life, before he went to
Hanover to study engineering and, later, painting. Although he failed academically in
both disciplines, he always had a tendency to look down on the picture stories that
brought him fame, and which were certainly his major contribution to world literature.
He continued to think that it was his vocation to paint, and his achievements in the field
were indeed respectable; but it was the combination of racy drawings with easy-flowing
verse of an almost proverbial character, reflecting life's malicious surprises, that secured
him lasting fame. In Germany, *Max und Moritz* ist still among the most widely read and
quoted children's books. "This is a rustic tale in verse of evil gusto, sardonic bathos, and
ultimately grotesque" (Arndt 1982:1). It is evident that the story has changed its
significance — for adult readers: children's reactions may still be what they were in 1865.
Lotze justly remarks that (1979:43 and 47):

> For many generations, *Max und Moritz* represented an unsophisticated tale of crime and punishment in a
> rural setting. Only after two world wars had thoroughly disrupted bourgeois society and forced people to
> take a new look at traditional values, did careful readers begin to see that Busch's criticism was directed also —
> perhaps even primarily — at his society.

> If we analyze the reactions of all the adults in this "childrens's epic," the same pattern of behavior emerges:
> each of these *petits bourgeois* reacts with the same vehemence and violence when his peace is disturbed.
> Neither the gentle tailor nor the good uncle and the wise teacher can accept such interference. Refusal to
> conform to the standards of society becomes a crime punishable by death. Creature comforts and material
> possessions assume supreme importance, so that the theft of fried chickens or pretzels, the destruction of a
> tobacco pipe and of a few grain sacks warrant execution.

It may be at least partly owing to such misunderstanding that interest in this twin rakes'
progress has been rather limited so far in other countries — but the story has also fallen
victim to a fate which is the worst that any literary work can meet abroad: bad translators.
The following section from the beginning of the fourth trick, short as it is, will bear out
my claim that it was not until very recently that congenial translations of *Max und Moritz,*
and of Wilhelm Busch in general, were undertaken (for full references see my bibliography, pp. 178-80).

Max und Moritz
Vierter Streich

Also lautet ein Beschluß:
Daß der Mensch was lernen muß. –
– Nicht allein das A-B-C
Bringt den Menschen in die Höh';
5 Nicht allein im Schreiben, Lesen
Übt sich ein vernünftig Wesen;
Nicht allein in Rechnungssachen
Soll der Mensch sich Mühe machen;
Sondern auch der Weisheit Lehren
10 Muß man mit Vergnügen hören. –
Daß dies mit Verstand geschah,
War Herr Lehrer Lämpel da. –
– Max und Moritz, diese beiden,
Mochten ihn darum nicht leiden;
15 Denn wer böse Streiche macht,
Gibt nicht auf den Lehrer acht. –
Nun war dieser brave Lehrer
Von dem Tobak ein Verehrer,
Was man ohne alle Frage
20 Nach des Tages Müh und Plage
Einem guten, alten Mann
Auch von Herzen gönnen kann. –

Anon (1874)

Deny the thatement if you can,
That something must be learnt by man. –
Not only simple A.B.C.
Can teach the world morality;
5 'Tis not enough to read and write,
For man endowed with reason's light;
Not only to arithmetic,
With hard wrought labour must he stick;
But he must learn with joy as well,
10 The truths that wisdom has to tell.
This, scientifically too,
Could Doctor Whackem help to do. –
– But Max and Moritz – pretty pair –
For this cause Whackem could not bear
15 As he who to such mischief looks
For pleasure, can't attend to books.
This teacher had a weakness slight,
He smoked tobacco every night.
This whim to humour, sure we may,
20 After the labours of the day,
Allow to be an old man's due,
And grant it with a good will too. –

C. T. Brooks 1871

An old saw runs somewhat so:
Man must learn while here below. –
Not alone the A, B, C,
Raises man in dignity;
5 Not alone in reading, writing,
Reason finds a work inviting;
Not alone to solve the double
Rule of Three shall man take trouble;
But must hear with pleasure Sages
10 Teach the wisdom of the ages.
Of this wisdom an example
To the world was Master Lämpel.
For this cause, to Max and Moritz
This man was the chief of horrors;
15 For a boy who loves bad tricks
Wisdom's friendship never seeks.
With the clerical profession
Smoking always was a passion;
And this habit without question,
20 While it helps promote digestion,
Is a comfort no one can
Well begrudge a good old man,
When the day's vexations close,
And he sits to seek repose. –

Walter Roome 1961

To this dictum we must cling:
man has got to learn something.
Not alone the ABC
raises you to some degree,
5 not alone to read and write
makes a human being bright,
not alone rithmetic is
basis for a life of bliss;
but to wisdom's teachings you
10 must with pleasure listen too. –
Teacher Temple's competence
taught to do so with good sense. –
Max and Maurice disagreed,
so they hated him indeed:
15 they like nasty tricks, therefore
teachers are what they ignore. –
Well, this teacher, good and smart,
to tobacco gave his heart.
Such an innocent delight
20 should, of course, be only right
for an old and decent man
who as hard works as he can. –

Karl E. Dietrich 1974

'Tis a law in every nation:
People need an education. –
Not alone the ABC
raises man to dignity,
5　not alone to read and write
is considered erudite,
and not just to count and figure
should one undertake with vigor,
but it's also wisdom's treasure
10　that should be absorbed with pleasure.
To effect this erudition,
that was Teacher Laempel's mission.
Max and Moritz, this bad pair,
had no use for him whate'er,
15　since all mischief-perpetrators
do not like their educators.
Laempel was to some degree
a tobacco devotee,
an enjoyment which, however,
20　after a long day's endeavor
and exertion no one can
well begrudge a good old man. –

Walter Arndt 1979

From on high it is ordained
That the human mind be trained –
Not alone the ABCs
Elevate it by degrees
5　Nor does writing competence
By itself make men of sense,
Nor will 'rithmetic in season
Satisfy aspiring reason:
Moral precepts, too, are needed –
10　To be heard with zeal and heeded.
Teachers see this wisely done.
Master Lampel here is one. –
Master Lampel's gentle powers
Failed with rascals such as ours;
15　For the evilly inclined
Pay preceptors little mind. –
Lampel now this honest teacher,
Loved to smoke his pipe – a creature
Comfort which, it may be said,
20　Once the day's hard load is shed,
No fair-minded person can
Hold against a dear old man. –

Anthea Bell 1975

Good children, in pursuit of knowledge,
Apply themselves, at school or college,
To learn their lessons, but a lot
Depends on teachers. It is not
5　Enough to learn your ABC,
Arithmetic, the Rule of Three,
Unless you learn good conduct too,
As good old Mr. Martin knew!
It was a custom and his rule,
10　When teaching in the local school,
To give his pupils good advice.
You might have thought that would be nice
For Max and Moritz, but they were
Ungrateful boys, as you shall hear,
15　And did not listen as they ought
To all the wisdom they were taught.
Now Mr. Martin's greatest pleasure
Was, in the evenings, at his leisure,
After the long day's work was done,
20　To smoke a pipe – or more than one –
Of best tobacco, which, he said,
Assisted him to clear his head.
His meerschaum was his dearest treasure,
And gave him solace in good measure.

Rudolf J. Wiemann 1982

Thus sets forth an ancient rule
That mankind must go to school. –
Not just to the alphabet
Does man clearly owe a debt;
5　Not just reading, writing season
Any being who can reason;
Not alone in 'rithmetic
Must man master every trick;
Gladly, too, for wisdom's teaching
10　Should he evermore be reaching. –
This to sensibly support,
Was one teacher Lampel's forte.
Max and Morry, plain to tell,
Therefore didn't like him well;
15　For all those who trick a lot,
Listen to the teacher not.
Now, this worthy teacherman
Was a strong tobacco fan
Which must merit one's consent
20　Where it helps a fine old gent
Find the needed relaxation
From a day of tribulation.

Wilhelm Busch himself appears not to have been particularly interested in what happened to his books in translation. There is a single substantial statement from him on the topic: Commenting on one of the worst translations ever made of one of his works, of *Die Fromme Helene,* which becomes in English *Naughty Jemina A Doleful Tale* ("It is", says W. Arndt's footnote, 1982:2), published by Nimmo, Edinburgh 1872, Busch states in a letter to his publisher Otto Bassermann, 6 November, 1972:

> The translation is funny and adequate in some parts, but stumbling and curiously artificial in others. This is wrong! Such things must be of appropriate polish and perfect form so that they are easily memorized and pronounced, a quality for which great diligence is necessary and an achievement of which I am quite proud. (Letter no. 148, translated)

The same much-quoted letter not only testifies to the great care that Busch devoted to every single line of his verse, but also to the importance he attached to the drawings, and the interplay of illustrations and text, as when he criticized the wording "With 180 illustrations" on the title-page of *Naughty Jemina,* comparing this with an advert reading: "FOR SALE: HOUSEKEY (HOUSE ATTACHED)".

With this verdict in mind, one wonders what he would have said about Morley's superficial revision of the poor anonymous translation of 1874 – combined with 'translated' drawings: lack-lustre illustrations redrawn by 'Jay' and published in Boston in 1932 – to commemorate the centenary of W. Busch's birth?

It would also be interesting to know whether W. Busch ever saw a copy of the picture stories that crudely imitated him in America and may have, as poor substitutes, stood in the way of a proper reception: "Upon W. R. Hearst's suggestion, Rudolph Dirks (1877–1968)began in 1897 to draw on *Max und Moritz* for his primitive but durable comic strip, *The Katzenjammer Kids,* naturalized during World War I as *The Captain and the Kids* (Arndt 1982: 1–2).

Literature

Arndt, Walter, *The Genius of Wilhelm Busch.* An English anthology edited and translated by W. A. Berkeley: Univ. of California Press, 1982.

Görlach, Manfred, ed., *Max und Moritz in deutschen Dialekten, Mittelhochdeutsch und Jiddisch.* Hamburg: Buske, 1982a.

–, *Max und Moritz polyglott,* deutsch, englisch, französisch, spanisch, italienisch, lateinisch. München: dtv, 1982b (1st–6th ed.).

Lotze, Dieter P., *Wilhelm Busch.* (Twayne's World Authors Series 525) Boston: G. K. Hall, 1979.

Translation: Possibilities and difficulties

A translator must attempt the impossible, and must not be deterred by the task. He will be aware of the fact that perfect equivalents in form (metre, rhythm, sound, rhyme etc.) as well as in matter (individual words, syntactic structures etc.) will be impossible to find and that if he wishes to translate efficiently it may well be necessary to rethink the relationship between the original drawings, the texts and the possibilities of the target language. One of

the special problems involved in this collection of translations was that the basic require-
ment for translating, viz. a perfect knowledge of the two languages in question, could not
always be met: how many people are there in the world, one wonders, with both
Cameroon Pidgin and German, or Northumbrian dialect and German at their command,
who would also be willing and competent to try a verse translation? Some of the
translators were in the difficult position of translating from a foreign language (of which,
in some cases, they had little knowledge) into a dialect or creole that was at least not their
normal means of everyday communication, and possibly not native to them at all. They
would then have to rely on the German text for metre and rhyme scheme, on the
drawings to provide inspiration for idiomatic expressions, on a prose translation into
English (which I supplied to guide correct understanding), and – cautiously – on existing
English translations of the story.

The difficulty of translating also increases with the distance between cultures. For a
Western European, the simple village story as told by Busch could have 'happened' in
each regional environment, and English and its dialects also have the formal prerequisites
in metre and rhyme to render the original structures; the most conspicuous difficulties
arise, in fact, from the cultural change that has occurred since 1865, a world without
motorcars, electric light, fridges and television. On the other hand, Busch's lexicon is
something that a dialect translator *can* handle. However, the situation is more complicat-
ed for Jamaica, West Africa, New Guinea – or the England of the 9th and 15th centuries.
While it is comparatively easy to think of solutions for *Sauerkraut* and *Maikäfer* in more
tropical cultures (see below), it is much more difficult to overcome limitations such as
non-existent traditions of rhymed poetry – whether in West African creoles or in Old
English. Metre and rhythm may not 'mean' the same, because the stress and tone systems
are too different, or the narrative structure of a culture may be too different to allow it to
be squeezed into tight and self-contained couplets. Luckily, there is less danger in
translating *Max und Moritz* into, say, Krio than there was in Thomas Decker's renderings
of Shakespeare – because expectations with such a serious work were much higher.
Readers will soon notice that it is also the small problems that count. It is more difficult to
start English lines with a beat, and then produce unstressed syllables in regular succession
and find the occasional female rhyme than in the original German (or in Middle English,
at a time when inflectional syllables were still available, if optional).
The adaptation of the text is of course shown in various substitutions of kinds of food,
animals and clothing. Thus the things that the boys steal are "taaties, neeps or peas" on
Shetland, "aringe an plom" on Jamaica, and "tinmit, banana" in New Guinea. What
Widow Bolte likes to combine with roast chicken is "sum hoorse-radeesh saace" in N, "a
drappie saatit kail" in A, "pease-brose" in G, "gowden creamy champit neeps" in L,
"some corly cale" in I, "pickle tings" in J, "shakpa" in K, "njamanjama" in C, and "bin,
na kon, na rais, na kabis" in T. And the crawlers that disturb Uncle's sleep are "maybugs"
in E, but "hundiclocks" in S, "golochs" in A, "bum-clokes" in L, G, and "dewels" in I; the
statement that "everyone knows what a ⎯ is" is as incorrect as it is for "gɔngrɔbi" (K),
"kɔkroch" (C) or "binatang" (T) – but the word "Maikäfer" has to be explained to
German children nowadays, so the difference is possibly not too great. The most obvious

indication of 'nativization' is in the selection of names – even though the most exotic translations (J, K, T, O) stick quite close to Busch's names. Here is a selection from the freer versions:

E	S	A	G	L	I	N	C
Mac	Jarm	Mac	Matt	Dod	Mack	Meyk	Tar
Murray	Jeemsie	Matthy	Malkie	Davie	Maurice	Moas	Tava
Bold	Baald	Bannock	Bloother	Bauld	Kelly	Boolor	Bol
Buck	Lamb	Gait	Boke	Goat	Buck	Seppy Grace	Kojo
Lample	Tait	Lintie	Lampwick	Duncan	Sample	Biffy Laasun	Matyu
Fred	Olly	Tam	James	Jock	Frank	–	Mangan
–	Magnie	Mains	Mac	Broun	John	Muck	–

Finally, there is the difficult question of how to render the stylistic differences of speakers in the story, mainly Mecke's Low German and the teacher's sociolect. The Scottish translators all select a rural dialect that is clearly distinct from the main variety: Annand (Northeastern/Lallans), Mulrine (East coast Sunday paper Scots/Glaswegian), McClure (Ayrshire/Northeastern), Herning (Whalsay/standard Shetland), but the most radical solution is Laycock's who makes him speak Motu rather than the other character's Tok Pisin. As for the teacher, his speech is slightly closer to standard in many versions; in C he speaks a mixture of pidgin and English – but does not achieve the baker's impeccable English!

I think the results collected in the present volume will confound pessimists who consider verse translations impossible. There are many lines in the various renderings just as good as Busch's – a few may even be better. The quality of a translation cannot be judged on the basis of purple patches, and the decision as to what renderings are adequate, congenial or ingenious will also vary from one reader to another. However that may be – here is a set of my favourite couplets (which the gentle reader is requested to identify and translate):

'Twas a wicked road and lang
Dod and Davie waled to gang.

Wan o these wʌz Wida Kelly –
here's hir lekness. Tik a skelly.

Vnder hegge, loo! thise tweyne
snoren dremynge of Cokayne.

Fin ere pliskies ull tae dee,
fa wad heed the dominie?

Oot wint he an in wint they –
Cat awaa, the meyce wud plyay.

Organan on swotum swege
hlynsodon mid gliwgefege,

Maist young fock an uncle hae
bidin in dis isles an sae

Masa mila dɔk dɛm kam
chɔp di pispis fine pas yam.

ɛn fɔ kɔt lɔng mata shɔt,
jɔy de na ɔl man im mɔt.

Neva stody, troble teacha,
neva pay no mine to preacha.

Reed the thoghtes on her face:
"Requiescant dum in paunche!"

And with sounds of "muck, muck, muck",
gone from sight is Master Buck.

When it's durty wurk ye need,
here's aye wullin hauns an heid.

Neb and hands and lugs and face
wad a bleckamoor disgrace;

Rikiraki! tupela i pilim
wil bilong wilwil i wilwilim.

Literary dialect

The dangers and limitations of using dialect, or other forms of non-standard speech, in writing are well known: the chosen variety may be deficient with regard to lexis and grammar, or it may be so closely associated with certain speakers and types of (low) life that it is little used in creative writing. For the linguist, literary texts provide special problems. If he is not acquainted with the dialect, it will be difficult to establish how 'realistic' or at least plausible the representation is, and in what ways the texts can be used as linguistic evidence. The normal thing, even with the best dialect writers, will be to expect a selective range of features (Ives 1971:147):

> Nearly all examples of literary dialect are deliberately incomplete; the author is an artist, not a linguist or a sociologist, and his purpose is literary rather than scientific. In working out his compromise between art and linguistics, each author has made his own decision as to how many of the peculiarities in his character's speech he can profitably represent; consequently, examples of literary dialect vary considerably in the extent to which they are "dialectal," and no very definite rules can be given regarding what to consider in that category.

The special feature of the *Max and Moritz* texts is that most were written by linguists rather than by active poets, but even their uses of the dialect do not exclude a compromise (such as in orthography or lexis) between what would be 'pure' dialect and what can be understood by the general reader. The concept of 'purity' itself presents a difficult problem. If the linguistic reality in Jamaica is a mixture of a former creole and approximations to standard English, then the linguist's use of creole may well be a form of language not actually encountered on the island today. Roland Bibby, in trying to use a 'purer' dialect than is normally heard today even in remote Northumbrian villages, consequently decided to write in a 19th-century dialect. Thus, each author is likely to select certain features – stressing similarities or differences between his variety and the related standard language in orthography, morphology, syntax, or lexicon; utilizing rare or obsolete words for their special appeal, or for the sake of the rhyme, or straining his syntax in order to fit in an expression too good to be left out.

In some cases, authors wrote in a dialect, or language, not their own. The dangers are possibly even more grievous here, but can be remedied by a judicious choice of informants who use (or once used) the language or dialect as their dominant form of speech: Derrick McClure, a native of Ayr, wrote the Northeastern Scots version; Derick Herning from Fife the Shetland poem; Loreto Todd not only her native N Irish text, but also the Cameroon Pidgin version, and Don Laycock from Australia the Tok Pisin translation. No such solution was – alas – possible for my Old and Middle English versions!

Literature

Blake, N. F., *Non-standard Language in English Literature*. London: Deutsch, 1981.

Brook, G. L., "Dialect and literature", in his *English Dialects*. London: Deutsch, [2]1965, pp. 184–209.

Craigie, William, "Dialect in literature", in *Essays by Divers Hands* 17 (Oxford, 1938), 69–91.

Ives, Sumner, "A theory of literary dialect", *Tulane Studies 2* (1950), 137–82; repr. in J. V. Williamson/V. M. Burke, *A Various Language*. New York: Holt, 1971, pp. 145–71.

Sullivan, J. P., "The validity of literary dialect: evidence from the theatrical portrayal of Hiberno-English forms", *Lang. Soc.* 9 (1980), 221–47.

E   *Standard English:* Mac and Murray by Elly Miller

With regard to the number of translations of *Max und Moritz* English, with ten different versions of the story so far, is well ahead of Latin, which comes next with seven known attempts (for details see Görlach 1982a). Most of the English translations were made during the last ten years, and these are the first that can be considered *adequate* renderings which succeed in carrying over enough of Busch's easy diction to enable a monoglot speaker of English to sense some of the attraction that the original has for many Germans. Among the recent translations those by Walter Arndt and Elly Miller appear to be the best. It is certainly no coincidence that both authors spent at least some of their early years in German-speaking surroundings (W. Arndt in Breslau, E. Miller in Vienna), where they made their first acquaintance with *Max und Moritz* in the original; after more than forty years in an English-speaking country, they are both still at home in the two cultures. Full appreciation of the achievements of both requires familiarity with all of their translations of W. Busch: Arndt's are now easily available (Arndt 1982), but E. Miller's still await publication in book form. I am very glad to have been able to include Arndt's text in the dtv polyglot edition and E. Miller's in the present collection: Mrs. Miller was kind enough to take up my suggestion of 1977 and attempt a new rendering.

As the English-speaking reader will soon notice, one of the characteristic differences between the Arndt and Miller versions (each made without knowledge of the other) is that Arndt's text has more memorable couplets, but that E. Miller's appears to be closer to Busch's uneventful everyday diction; the ratio of Germanic rhyme words, for instance, is much higher than in Arndt.

Elly Miller was born in Vienna in 1928, fled to England after the *Anschluss* in 1938, and was educated in London and at Oxford. After her Oxford M. A. she worked as a research assistant, then for Oxford University Press, New York, before she became Editor and Director of Phaidon Press, London. She founded Harvey Miller Publishers in 1971 and has been its Editorial Director ever since. Apart from her interest in music, which includes the writing of verse and songs, she has translated, over the years, most of Busch's picture stories and poems. Elly Miller is married, with three children and four grand-children.

English dialects

England, and from the 17th century onwards, Great Britain, has been more monolingual than France (Britain's Celtic languages have been rapidly retreating along the fringes especially since the 19th century); it is also much more centralized than Italy and Germany, whose statehood dates only from the 19th century. This meant that a uniform standard spread quickly from London, in the printed form, increasingly also affecting the spoken form of the language. Dialect was, in consequence, regarded quite early on as a linguistic marker of the less educated. Elizabethan literature shows that this was already the evaluation of the 16th century: Puttenham (1589) warns prospective poets against using any speech but the educated variety of "London and sixty miles around", and Edgar, dressed as a peasant in Shakespeare's *King Lear,* also adopts the clown's Zummerzet stage dialect. Regional speech has remained in low esteem for writing, and not even the English Romantic writers made use of it in their poetry. It was the example of the Scotsman, Robert Burns, that sparked off a minor wave of dialect poetry in the 19th century; there was, however, a more substantial representation of regional speech in the novels of the period.

Among the English dialects, those of the north (Lancashire, Northumbria, Yorkshire) and of the southern periphery (Southwestern in Devon, Southeastern in East Anglia) have, because of their greater distance from London, and being less closely linked with the standardizing centres, best retained their distinctive qualities. Even here, however, the characteristic features in morphology, syntax and vocabulary are being eroded very quickly. One would not be far wrong in claiming that the last generation of speakers who lived in 'intact' dialect surroundings was that just before the turn of the century, when broad dialect was not only a characteristic of old, non-mobile, male rural speakers, but – as the popularity of dialect almanacs from urban Yorkshire tells us – also widespread in the new urban conglomerations.

Of course, daily speech in England's north still differs a lot from urban southern English, but today this is rather a matter of pronunciation, in the main, and where other elements of the old dialect have been incorporated into modern urban speech, they are frequently found in the stigmatized speech of the less educated. This contrasts strongly with the nostalgic reverence in which the lost 'good old dialect' is held.

My various attempts to commission translations from Devon, East Anglia, Lancashire and Yorkshire have failed. But even if they had been successful, their status for an English speaker would have been much more 'eccentric' than dialect poetry is for a German reader. Thus, although a proper geographical balance within England, or within the United Kingdom, was not possible in this collection, I am still very glad that England is represented.

Literature

Bailey, R. W./M. Görlach, eds., *English as a World Language.* Ann Arbor, 1982.
Trudgill, Peter, ed., *Languages of Britain.* Cambridge: UP, 1984.
Wakelin, Martyn F., *English Dialects. An Introduction.* London: Athlone, [2]1977.

N   *Northumberland:* Meyk un Moas by Roland Bibby

Northumbria as a dialect region originally covered the complete area north of the Humber, one of Britain's oldest and most important dialect boundaries. Because of the political separation of Scotland after 1006/18, and increasing animosity across the Border in the 14th century (Edward I and Robert Bruce), the linguistic area of Northumbria became limited to the English portions, and since the dialects of Lancashire and Yorkshire also developed independent features, dialectologists are now happy to refer to 'Northumbrian' as the speech of the two counties of Tyne & Wear (the urban concentration of Newcastle, Gateshead and Sunderland) on the one hand and Northumberland (the more or less rural parts east of the Pennines) on the other. These county boundaries point up one of the most impressive contrasts in England: the heavy industry of the conglomeration with its 1.2 million speakers as against its sparsely inhabited hinterland to the north and west, in which the biggest towns – great names in British history such as Alnwick, Berwick or Hexham – have some 8.–15.000 inhabitants each. This population imbalance has, of course, also had its linguistic consequences: 'Tyneside' is now considered to be more or less identical with 'Northumbrian' by the average Englishman – the linguistic tail now wags the dog. In such a neighbourhood of urban centres, the decline of the old dialect has been drastic. Roland Bibby has therefore in his translation consistently used the dialect of a time when central concepts of everyday life still had their dialect designations – and he is further justified in doing so because a poem of 1865 *can* of course be translated into pre-industrial village speech. Stressing the colloquial nature of the text rather than attempting a very close translation, he has transposed the story into just such a rural mid-Northumbrian dialect of a century ago, in preference to present-day urban 'Geordie', which would not have matched the village scene of the boys' exploits. His version needs to be read aloud (or listened to on the accompanying cassette). This mitigates the quaint effect of the spelling which R. Bibby chose in order to render as closely as possible the phonetic qualities of the dialect sounds, especially the vowels. One of the famous features of the dialect is the 'Northumbrian burr', which is here represented by italic *r* wherever it occurs.

Roland Bibby was born in 1917 at Morpeth, Northumberland, where he still lives. After the War (which he largely spent in India and Burma with the Border Regiment) he took a degree in social studies and taught history from 1952–78. He has for long been chairman, now vice-president of Morpeth Antiquarian Society, organizer of the annual Morpeth Northumbrian Gathering, editor-publisher of the *Northumbriana Quarterly,* and active for the use and preservation of his dialect in local radio, television and in the press, to which he contributes a weekly column and occasional articles. His three books are all on Northumbrian history and folklore. R. Bibby is widowed, with a son and a daughter, both teachers and Northumbrian musicians.

I *Northern Ireland* Mack an Maurice by Anthony Seymour and Loreto Todd

Since around 1600 there have been three forms of language competing in N Ireland: Gaelic, Ulster Scots and Midulster English. An organized colonization ("Plantation of Ulster") forced the Celts out of various regions and brought some 100.000 Scots and 20.000 English (mainly from the western counties) into Ulster by 1641, making the region more English-speaking than the southern Irish counties. The ratio of Gaelic speakers has been declining ever since; there are no native speakers of the language left in present-day N Ireland. But the fact that English was acquired by many patchily and informally means that even today many features of Celtic origin still 'shine through' in the

English of former Gaelic-speaking areas, especially in pronunciation, in the syntax and in the high ratio of Celtic loanwords. Many features of the I text will in fact remind readers of the Irish English employed by some writers of the Irish Renaissance, especially by J. M. Synge in his *Playboy of the Western World* (1907), where he made a consistent effort to employ the Gaelicized English of the west of Ireland for his dialogues.

The present translation was first written by A. N. Seymour, who partly relied on Brook's English rendering (his influence is still easy to detect). This version was thoroughly rephrased by L. Todd – and tried out with great success on a five-year-old native speaker of the dialect! As regards spelling, note that in the I text the letter ʌ is used for all cases where the sound of *but* is intended but where there was no unambiguous way to indicate that the dialect pronunciation diverged from the standard; *fʌll* 'full' thus rhymes with *hull*, *bʌsh* 'bush' with *hush*.

Anthony N. Seymour was born in 1942 in Antrim in N. Ireland. He was educated at Protestant schools before going on to the Queen's University of Belfast, where he gained a First in English Language and Literature. He spent four years teaching in Nigeria and has been teaching at Limavady Grammar School, Derry, for fourteen years. A. N. Seymour has published plays, poetry and short stories locally.

Loreto Todd was born in 1942 in Coalisland, a village in Co. Tyrone, N Ireland. She was educated at Catholic schools before attending the Queen's University of Belfast where she read English (M. A. on Cameroon Pidgin) before she went on to Leeds for her Ph. D. She spent four years in Cameroon and combines a rare interest, personal and professional, in Gaelic, N Irish English, Cameroon Pidgin and English-based pidgins and creoles in general, a topic on which she has written two important textbooks (Todd 1974, 1984).

Literature

Adams, G. B.†/Loreto Todd, *Northern Ireland*. (Varieties of English around the World) Amsterdam: Benjamins, forthcoming.
Ó Muirithe, Diarmaid, ed., *The English Language in Ireland*. Dublin: Mercier, 1977.
Ulster Dialects. An Introductory Symposium. Holywood: Ulster Folk Museum, 1964.

Scotland

Some knowledge of Scottish history is useful in explaining the present-day linguistic situation and in contextualizing the four translations. Originally Celtic-speaking like the rest of Britain, Scotland was slowly anglicized from the southeast. The eastern Border counties were Anglo-Saxon-speaking in the 9th century, Edinburgh and the Lothians in the 10th century, and by the 13th century the expansion had reached the Celtic Border, along the western limits of the mountains, which has ever since divided the Lowlands from the Highlands. The linguistic development in Scotland was similar to that in England: from the 15th century onwards the dialect of the capital, Edinburgh, was made into a standard language in which, mainly between 1430 and 1570, a substantial corpus of literature of remarkable quality and range was written. Political factions, the uncertain prestige of Standard Scots as against English, the willingness even among the best Scots writers to borrow freely from the English language, the minimal production of Edinburgh printing houses – all add up to the fact that the future of Scots was already threatened in the later 16th century. One of the most important factors was that no printed Bible in Scots was available; if it had been, it might have further standardized the language – as other Bible translations have done for other languages. When in 1579 a law made the possession of a Bible compulsory for every householder of a certain income, this had to be a Bible in English, with the inevitable result that the Scots increasingly regarded their own 'leid' as the spoken medium fit for everyday communication, but English as appropriate for all forms of writing and for conversations of a more formal character. (The social history of Scots has close parallels to Low German). From the 17th century onwards, then, we must distinguish at least five types of speech:

1. Gaelic, uncontested as the single language of the Highlands until the mid-18th century, but rapidly decreasing ever since.
2. Scottish dialects as they had developed directly from Middle English roots (cf. text A). These were the medium of expansion until the 17th century (Orkney and Shetland lost their Scandinavian language from the 16th century on, replacing it with Scots dialect, with admixtures from the islands' Scandinavian language, Norn; cf. Text S).

3. Forms of English as written and spoken in Scotland. Whereas there was little alternative to English for written use after 1603, spoken forms of English were slow to catch on, spreading from educated circles in 18th-century Edinburgh society, and making inroads elsewhere from the 19th century onwards, mostly because of the relentless attitude towards dialect adopted by the school authorities. Also, English (rather than Scots) generally was the new language imposed on the Highlands, so that the Celtic Border today is still a linguistic boundary, which however now divides Scots dialects to the east and Highland English to the west of it.

4. The fully developed literary language of the 16th century continued to be used, though reduced to a trickle. After 1700, poets like Ramsay (for pastoral and mock elegies), Fergusson (Edinburgh scenes), Burns (folksongs and ballads) and Sir Walter Scott (dialogues, especially in some of his novels on 18th-century Scotland) fully exploited the possibilities of their respective genres (with some compromising towards English because of a potential English readership), but they did not try to give back to Scots the full range of functions of a standard language. With the increasing loss of dialect words in the urbanized region of Lothian and adjacent areas – on which the literary language is historically based – the writing in literary Scots (Lallans) has become less and less intelligible to Scotsmen, especially if (as in some Lallans writing) the proportion of obsolete words is markedly high (but cf. text L).

5. The Industrial Revolution brought with it the urbanization of large portions of the Scottish population. However, in contrast to the many industrial conglomerations of England, there was only one centre in Scotland: Glasgow/Central Clydeside, its 1.7 million inhabitants now making up a third of the total population. The very poor living conditions and the fact that the 'better-educated' left it to the poor to speak urban Glaswegian has given to this form of speech very low prestige. (As elsewhere in the world, rural dialects are praised for their pureness and genuineness, as against 'corrupted' urban varieties.) (Cf. text G)

I here evade the issue of whether the four Scots translations are to be described as representing dialects of the Scots or the English language. Whereas the first possibility is certainly true from a historical point of view, it is also true that the standard end of the present dialect continuum is the English of the schools, the media, administration, and written forms in general.

Literature

Aitken, A. J./Tom McArthur, eds., *Languages of Scotland*. Edinburgh: Chambers, 1979.
Görlach, Manfred, ed., *Focus on: Scotland*. Amsterdam: Benjamins, 1985.
Grant, William/J. M. Dixon, *Manual of Modern Scots*. Cambridge: UP, 1921.
McClure, J. D., et al., *The Scots Language: Planning for Modern Usage*. Edinburgh: Ramsay Head, 1980.
Murison, David, *The Guid Scots Tongue*. Edinburgh: Blackwood, 1977.
Robinson, Mairi, ed., *The Concise Scots Dictionary*. Aberdeen: UP, 1985.

L   *Literary Scots (Lallans):* Dod and Davie by J. K. Annand

Lallans writing in the 20th century is an impressive illustration of the fact that a literary tradition can be kept alive over the centuries though the basis of the spoken dialect is giving away. Lallans writers have, of course, seen the problem and advocated:

a) a functional expansion of the language (see the prose writing, which includes book reviews and other technical discussions, in the all-Scots magazine *Lallans,* edited by J. K. Annand until 1983);

b) a continuous enrichment of the Lallans lexicon by borrowing from the spoken dialects or, where necessary, creating new compounds and derivations, and

c) working for the acceptance of Scots among the Scottish people.

The first two moves have not been unsuccessful, but the Scots have never made the language question, and their identification with "Our ain leid" a matter of central concern.

Jim Annand, or J. K. Annand in his writings, was born in 1908 in Midlothian. For a long time, he has been one of the best-known writers in Scots, which he uses with natural ease. Most of his energy in more recent years has gone into *Lallans,* which he founded in 1973. Here is what he himself has to say on writing in Scots (in Görlach 1985:187):

> What kinna leid, then, does a native Scotch writer turn til the day? Does he write in English or in Scotch, or in baith leids? And whatna kinna Scotch should he yaise? Here I maun speak only for mysel, but I hae nae dout that a wheen ither scrievers hae tane a siclike gait. For poetry the chyce was geyan easy. I first tried the English, but never made muckle o't. My ettles in Scotch had mair success. What wey that was sae, I canna richtly say. I gat as muckle pleisure out o readin guid poetry in English as I did wi guid poetry in Scotch. Aiblins it was that in spite o my schuilin, I was never richtly at hame in English. My thochts seem to gang mair eithly in Scotch. Hou be it, I hae kept on at the Scotch, and sic poems as I hae ettled in English dinna seem to hae the same success.

His active work for Scots is also outstanding for the diversity and high quality of his own writing. Among these are many translations from various languages such as German, French and Latin (he has translated portions of the *Carmina Burana* into modern Scots) and especially his writing for children: this was an excellent control against writing in an archaic or artificial style, since children would have plainly revolted against unintelligible poems. He also makes the understanding of his texts easier for non-Scottish readers by using an orthography much closer to the British standard than his spoken Scots would justify.

G   *Glasgow:* Matt an Malkie by Stephen Mulrine

With the rapid expansion of Glasgow, first a commercial and small industrial centre in the 18th century, and from 1830–40 as a centre for steel and coal production, the face of the city and the composition of its inhabitants probably changed more drastically than any other city in Britain. Great numbers of immigrants poured in from the neighbouring counties of Renfrew, Ayr and Lanark, but many also came from the Highlands, forced out by the Clearances, and most of these were Gaelic speakers. After the great potato famines in 1846 and 1847, the Irish made up almost half of the newcomers; again, most of these had a Celtic (and Catholic) background, but many were returning to the country of their forefathers – the majority of 17th-century settlers in N Ireland had come from the west of Scotland. Glasgow has ever since remained the most populous Scottish city: every third Scotsman now lives in the city or the surrounding conglomeration. There are contrasts in close proximity: the "guid auld leid" of the Ayrshire poet Robert Burns, born some 35 miles south of Glasgow, and the non-prestigious urban dialect of present-day Glasgow; the "bonnie banks" of Loch Lomond only 15 miles northwest of the Gorbals. Since the nineteen-sixties, there has been a tradition of using Glasgow dialect for jocular concoctions *(Parliamo Glasgow)* on the one hand, and also for serious poetry and play-writing on the other. Together, they have helped create orthographic conventions for the otherwise unwritten dialect (Macafee 1983:39f.).

Stephen Mulrine, born in Glasgow in 1937 and educated at Glasgow and Edinburgh universities, where he studied English and Scots literature and language, was one of the young Glasgow poets who in the early seventies consistently used the dialect in some of their poetry – one of the best-known modern Glasgow poems is his "Whit'll ye dae when the wee Malkies come?". He deliberately chose broad urban speech for his translation, too; the only concession to antiquity here made is that the number of old Scots words used is higher than would normally be heard in a Glasgow playground.

Literature

Macafee, Caroline, *Glasgow*. (Varieties of English around the World). Amsterdam: Benjamins, 1983.

Morgan, Edwin, "Glasgow speech in recent Scottish literature", in J. Derrick McClure, ed., *Scotland and the Lowland Tongue*. Aberdeen: UP, 1983, pp. 195–208.

A *Northeastern Scots (Aberdeenshire):* Mac an Matthy by J. Derrick McClure

The Northeast, i.e. the triangle formed by a line through Dundee, Fraserburgh and Inverness, jutting out towards the east and having its western boundary defined by the Celtic Border, has long been considered by many as the ideally 'pure' form of Scots, its 'Doric' dialect. The region can also claim John Barbour, Archdeacon of Aberdeen, the first known Scottish poet (c. 1375) – but the 15/16th-century standard was of course based on dialects closer to the capital. However, Aberdeenshire has never seen the early inroads made by the prestigious English language in the 18th century, and the development of a low-prestige sociolect is much more recent than in Glasgow. But even in rural areas, education has levelled away much of the characteristic dialect; Dieth described the ensuing compromise forms as early as 1932 (p. xviii):

> The young folk have no sooner escaped the dominie's rod, than they slip back, unconsciously, to their natural way of talking. The return, however, is not complete.

Wölck found by 1962 that his informants even in small villages were bidialectal, and though taking pride in their dialect were all able to converse in standard English (Wölck 1965). Although the dialect lexicon was much affected, the northeast can still claim regional speech widespread in some intimate domains – and superb dialect writing, which ranges from Alexander Scott's Lallans enriched with Aberdeen lexis to Flora Garry's more traditional themes in a more localised dialect.

John Derrick McClure was born in Ayr in 1944, studied at Glasgow (M.A.) and Edinburgh (M. Litt.) and taught at Tübingen and Ottawa universities before he took up a lecturership at King's College, Aberdeen, where he has been teaching English (and Scottish!) language ever since 1972. He is one of the few scholars with a detailed knowledge of the history and present-day functions of Scots, and has written extensively on the literary uses of Scots, from the 16th century through Galt to 20th-century poetry and prose. He is married, with three boys.

Writing in a dialect not his own was a special challenge for J. D. McClure; he wishes to acknowledge the kind help of native speakers who improved the accuracy of his translation: David Murison, Flora Garry, Louis Barclay and T. M. Allan; and Alastair Taylor who read the text for the cassette recording.

Literature

Dieth, Eugen, *A Grammar of the Buchan Dialect. I: Phonology – Accidence.* Cambridge: Heffer, 1932.

Donaldson, William/Douglas Young, eds., *Grampian Hairst*. Aberdeen: UP, 1981 (anthology).

McClure, J. D., *Northeastern Scots*. (Varieties of English around the World) Amsterdam: Benjamins, forthcoming.

Wölck, Wolfgang, *Phonematische Analyse der Sprache von Buchan*. Heidelberg: Winter, 1965.

S *Shetland:* Jarm an Jeemsie by Derick Herning

When Margaret of Denmark married James III of Scotland in 1469, Orkney and Shetland formed the security for her dowry; although they never became officially part of Scotland, James III and his successors always acted as if the islands were theirs to keep. An unbroken period of Scandinavian culture, which had lasted from the settlement of the islands in the 9th century, was slowly coming to an end. However, it was only after the Reformation and Scottish expansion in the late 16th and the whole of the 17th centuries that the Kirk, the school and commerce firmly settled the Scots language in the islands. Scots was considered superior to the native Norn, even at a time when Scots itself had come under attack from English, which in turn replaced the dialect in more formal functions from the 18th century on. Yet, despite rapid anglicisation, especially after the establishment of the Board Schools (1872), not only the dialect, but also remnants of the Norn language have survived to a surprising degree. When the Faroese scholar J. Jakobsen collected these remains in 1839–95, he was able to record some 10,000 items (however limited their distribution already was at that time). Increasing mobility, cheap reading matter and the influence of the media have reduced the knowledge and the functions of Shetland dialect in the 20th century – until at least quite recently when islanders came to identify with it, partly to ward off the all-pervading influence of North Sea Oil, and the dialect has thus regained a certain degree of respectability. Radio Shetland is one of the few local stations using dialect (along with English) for some of its programmes. Such a remarkable survival of the dialect, in spite of small numbers of speakers – a mere 20,000 on 17 inhabited islands of Shetland, 17,500 on 24 inhabited islands of the Orkneys – is of course partly to be explained by the great isolation of the islands until very recently.

Derick Herning was born in 1932 in Kirkcaldy, Fife. He studied German and French at Edinburgh University, did his national service as a linguist in Russian, and after taking his diploma in education, taught in Fife and Glasgow (1956–62) and in adult education in Mainz, Germany (1963–67). He has been the principal teacher of German and Norwegian at Anderson High School, Lerwick, since 1967. His various hobbies include jogging and bird-watching as well as yoga, music, drama and – of course – languages.

D. Herning would like to thank June Johnson, Danny Jamieson and especially John J. Graham for help and advice in the translation work, and June Johnson for reading the text for the cassette recording.

Literature

Graham, John J., *The Shetland Dictionary*. Stornoway, Lewis: Thule, 1979 repr. Lerwick: Shetland Publishing Co., 1984 (includes an introduction with a history of the dialect).

–/ T. A. Robertson, eds., *Nordern Lichts. An Anthology of Shetland Verse and Prose*. Lerwick: Shetland County Council, 1964.

Robertson, T. A./ John J. Graham, *Grammar and Usage of the Shetland Dialect*. Lerwick: Shetland Times, 1952.

Pidgin and creole languages

As a direct result of the colonial expansion of various European powers and their plantation system, pidgin languages arose in West Africa, the Caribbean, in South and Southeast Asia and – much later – in the Pacific region. Certain conditions must be met for such languages to develop: speakers of three or more languages, but none in common, will construct, from the grammars of their native languages and scraps of European languages, a lingua franca for their basic communicative needs, a speech form that is nobody's mothertongue, without a written or unwritten norm, fluctuating, and possibly forgotten as soon as the need for it no longer exists. Such a language can be expected to have the following characteristics:

1. a very narrow range of functions (plantation, trade, etc.);
2. a minimal lexicon (of around 1,000 words), the individual words having quite frequently a meaning wider than, or at least divergent from, that of the (European) source language;
3. a reduced syntactical structure and normally no inflectional morphology;
4. a phonology with many features carried over from the mothertongues, such as possible reduction of the phoneme inventory (with resulting homonyms); reduction

of clusters, especially at beginning and ends of words; retention of tone distinctions
and intonational patterns, often complementing the lack of syntactical distinctions;
5. largely non-European pragmatic rules.

Educational facilities for slaves were minimal, and since the 'proper' form of the respective European language was largely out of reach for them, many of the pidgins came to be accepted as compromise languages in which children were brought up. This nativization of a language is known as creolization; it happened quite early in Jamaica (18th century), but is more uncertain in West Africa (where the number of pidgin speakers who speak the language as a second language greatly exceeds mother tongue speakers). Although the expansion of a pidgin language, i.e. the extension of its functions to new domains with the resulting increase in the lexicon and syntactical differentiation, can happen without creolization (this is happening in New Guinea), such expansion is a natural consequence of creolization. If in this process the related European language is available, it is normal to supplement the creole's lexicon and syntax from that source (especially since the prestige of the European standard language would suggest this procedure): the resulting process of decreolization will then bring the creole language still closer to the standard, or rather, standard and creole features will form a post-creole continuum, in which the ratio of creole features will usually be determined by the educational standing of the speaker-hearer, and the formality of the situation – in fact, conditions of use not unlike the distribution of dialect versus standard in many European countries.

The justification for including such pidgin/creole versions here is the historical relationship that these languages have with English and which is still clearly evident from their lexicons. Although Krio, Cameroon Pidgin and Tok Pisin must be classified as distinct languages, and not dialects of English, the case of Jamaican Creole makes it clear that decreolization can lead to a point where it is appropriate to categorize such a language as a 'dialect' of English again.

Literature

Görlach, Manfred, "'Creolizing' a German children's book", paper, 2. Essener Kolloquium zu "Kreolsprachen und Sprachkontakten", Nov. 1985, to be published in *Proceedings*.
Hymes, Dell, ed., *Pidginization and Creolization of Languages*. Cambridge: UP, 1971.
Todd, Loreto, *Pidgins and Creoles*. London: Routledge, 1974.
–, *Modern Englishes: Pidgins and Creoles*. Oxford: Blackwell, 1984.
Valdman, Albert, ed., *Pidgin and Creole Linguistics*. Bloomington: Indiana UP, 1977.

J   *Jamaican Creole:* Max an Marris by Jean D'Costa

Cromwell's conquest of Jamaica in 1655 marks the breakthrough of English power – and of the English language – in the Caribbean: even though the peripheral Barbados had been English from 1625, and Belize from 1638, and some minor island possessions (Anguilla, Antigua, Barbuda, Montserrat, Nevis) also preceded the conquest of Jamaica, only the

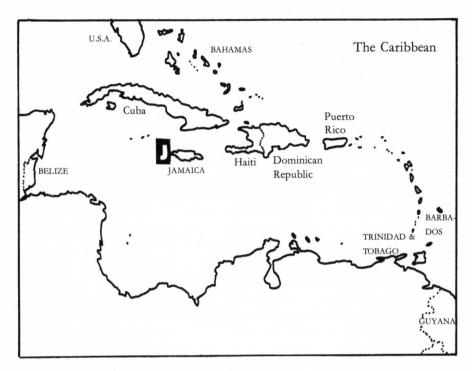

latter success firmly established Britain in the region. However, even today's figures show that English ranks only third among the languages of the Caribbean. It thus comes, with 4.5 million speakers, after Spanish (18 million) and French (5.5 million), and indeed Spanish has twice as many speakers as the other languages put together. And the hinterland to the west and south is also staunchly Spanish-speaking. Among the ten states with English as an official language, Jamaica is the giant with its 2.1 million inhabitants, most states being much smaller (Trinidad & Tobago 1.1, Barbados .25, Grenada .11, Dominica .11 million etc.). Since no native Indians were alive on Jamaica in 1655, and the English forced out all Spaniards (drawing settlers from Barbados and Guyana, and of course from Europe, and importing huge numbers of slaves) the island has a comparatively 'uncomplicated' linguistic history: with the founding of huge sugar plantations, Jamaican whites became immensely rich, but greatly dominated in numbers by their black slaves, who adopted the English-based pidgin as their mother tongue, and thus creolized it in the 18th century, affecting in turn the speech habits of Jamaican whites. With liberation and general education in the 19th century, the *patois* came to be despised by the emerging Black middle class. More educated speakers aimed at standard English as best they could, and this decision was reinforced by church, schools, colonial administration and public opinion in general. As a result, the two linguistic systems were interfused in daily use, with clear prestige differences between the creole and standard ends of the continuum, but also with most speakers able to use the full range of linguistic shades (to switch style) according to the formality of the speech event. Such shift upwards is exemplified in the J text by 21f. *verse: worse* (with /r/); 69 *Lawd* (cf. *Laad);* 204,215 *learn(in);* 204 *study* (with /ʌ/), all from the domains of church and school. Attitudes towards creole have been ambivalent since Independence in 1962. Even today some older middle class speakers jealously guard the correctness of Jamaican English grammar against 'destructive' influences from what some would regard as 'ghetto' language. But many, especially younger speakers below 35, are now consistent users of the middle-of-the-road (mesolectal) variety, which also dominates in schools – the playground language being mostly broad patois. Bidialectalism has been advocated in education since the late sixties (Craig 1976), and primary school teachers emphasize this dual nature of language usage.

Although radio, television and the theatre have shown an increasing use of mesolectal speech, the use of (broad) creole in print has been limited so far. However, there have been successful attempts at employing creole in creative writing, especially in poetry and in dialogues in novels, since the beginning of this century, and the local public has grown fond of such uses. The language of these literary texts is, however, difficult to interpret for an outsider (and even for Jamaicans accustomed to Standard English spelling): the denseness of a writer's creole can vary with his artistic intentions, with his willingness to compromise for the sake of international intelligibility – and it can indicate shades existing within the post-creole continuum. Although there is no standard creole orthography, aspects of standardization are beginning to appear with the increase of creole texts in the last ten years.

Various grammatical features of the J text (as, of course, of the K, C, T texts) make it clear that the language used is a creole and not an English (dialect) form. It will be in order to point out such features in J – and request the reader to detect them in the K, C, T texts:

1. (variable) non-marking of inflections:
   plural: *tree en* (35) 'three hens', but *feelins* (81), *tings* (106); creole marking by-*dem: de wretch-dem* (386).
   genitive: *Mass Bock wife* (195) etc.
   3rd person: *she no see* (109).
2. Absence of tense (unmarked verb forms throughout). Aspect markers:
   a) *a* for 'continuous': *a look* (12), *a growl* (125), *a hais* (379), etc., but verb + *-in* frequent.
   b) *gwine* for 'future': *gwine pay* (130), etc.; but also *wi* 'will'.
   c) *did* for 'anterior': *did look, did keep* (34f.), *did fly* (49) (cf. 88, 399, 402).
   d) *don* for 'completive': *don nyam* (51).
3. Absence of passive construction: *bes pipe mek* (238), *non leave* (264).
4. Negation: *no,* without DO-periphrasis: *she no see* (109).
5. Copula: Ø preceding adjectives (271–2); *a* preceding nouns: *a fun* (335).
6. Adverbs: unmarked (277).
7. Personal pronouns: one common form, as in *him* = 'he, his, him; her' (246–51); *in bed* 65), but *she, ar* are usual. For the possessive *fi* + alternates: *fi-yuh* 'your' (128), *fi-im* (148), *fi-dem* (8).

As regards phonology, the following differences from Standard English are obvious; they can also serve to identify equivalents and thus make some glosses unnecessary:

1. Initial clusters are often, final clusters frequently reduced: *'tep, 'tring, 'tretch, 'crape; res(t), nex(t), min(d), ruos* 'roast'.
2. /ɵ, ð/ are *t, d: tief, mout, dem, wid*.
3. /r/ is not realized after vowel and preceding consonants: *yaad, lawd,* but *muor* 'more'.
4. /h/ is not phonemic, but variable according to emphasis: *aad* 'hard'; *hincrease*.
5. Short vowels: the sound in *but* is close to /o/; that in *body, off* is /a(:)/: *bady, aaf, saaf* 'soft', *daag* 'dog'.
6. E. /ei/ in *name* is /ie/: *niem, siem, tielor;* /ou/ in *soul* is /uo/: *suol, fuor,* /nuo/ 'know'; /oi/ often /wai/: *bway, bwail* 'boil'.

For these characteristics compare 89f.:

> N*ie*kid now p*a*n kitchen t*ie*ble
> K*o*t *a*r s*uo*l m*uo*r *d*an she *ie*ble.

The sound of the language is very difficult to portray, whatever orthography one uses, and only listening to the cassette will make the intended qualities quite clear. Rather than adopt the phonemic spelling developed by F. G. Cassidy for Jamaican Creole, we decided to use spellings closer to Standard English so as not to endanger the intelligibility for the non-linguist. Therefore *ie* is used only where the English equivalent remains recognizable (*ieble, niem;* but not in *ways* /wiez/, etc.). This inconsistency is to be regretted, but is unavoidable. It also means that several rhymes do not look like rhymes, but are perfect in sound (cf. 337f. *kiek: ache;* 393f. *trough: aaf*). Here is, for comparison, the Prologue in strictly phonemic spelling:

> Lisn now, som pikni bad:
> Tuu bwai ruud so tel dem mad!
> Aal mi taak a so-so truut:
> Maks an Maris in dem yuut
> Neva stodi, chroble tiicha,
> neva pie no main to priicha.
> Dem so fiesti in dem wiez
> Fi-dem mowt shud wash wid jiez.
> Kook-nat saafa dan dem hed
> Skuul miin nottn tu di dred.
> Wies a taim fi stodi buk

> Wen ruudnes yu a luk.
> Skuul an cherch a ignarans
> Wen mango-taim bring yu chaans.
> Klaim chrii tiif arinj an plom
> Bot in skuul dem def an dom.
> Aal dem gud fa iz fi tiiz
> Huu som eva dem main pliiz.
> Taim, yu nuo, langa dan ruop,
> Sipl muor dan washin suop.
> Ku di pikcha an di vers
> We dem gaan fram bad tu wers.

Jean d'Costa was born in Jamaica in 1937, grew up with creole and English, and was educated in Jamaica up to university level. After her Oxford M. Litt. in English literature (1962), she taught linguistics and English language history at the University of the West Indies for fifteen years, when she also worked on language school curricula and as a consultant with various teachers' colleges. She now teaches at Hamilton College, Clinton, N. Y. Jean d'Costa has published three children's novels (Longman Caribbean), which won her an award from the Jamaica Reading Association in 1978. At present she is working on a historical novel on 18th-century Jamaica and is collecting early creole texts.

Literature

Alleyne, Mervyn C., *Comparative Afro-American: An Historical-Comparative Study of English-Based Afro-American Dialects in the New World*. Ann Arbor: Karoma, 1980.

Bailey, B. L., *Jamaican Creole Syntax: A Transformational Approach*. Cambridge: UP, 1966.

Cassidy, F. C., *Jamaica Talk: Three Hundred Years of the English Language in Jamaica*. New York: St Martin's Press, 1961.

–/ R. B. LePage, *Dictionary of Jamaican English*. Cambridge: UP, 1967, ²1980.

Lawton, David L., "English in the Caribbean", in Bailey/Görlach 1982:251–80.

West Africa

The complex linguistic situation of West Africa is of course not even touched upon here – there are more than a thousand indigenous languages and four European colonial languages, some of these with various forms of pidgins and creoles used alongside them, all spoken with varying degrees of perfection, some (but only a minority) also written. Whereas the target for educated English has – with the single exception of Liberia – always been British English, and educated West Africans take pride in the Oxford purity of their language, various forms of English and pidgin have withstood the correcting influences of the schools and missions. It does in fact appear likely that a West African standard is emerging for English which will be more hospitable to local usages. As in Jamaica, but with less of a continuum so far between English and its pidgin, a more or less coherent belt of pidgin English has existed along the West African coast from Gambia to Cameroon since the 17th century. Of course, the distribution of the language differs from nation to nation: there is less of it in Ghana, and even less in the French-speaking states Senegal, Ivory Coast and Benin. All varieties of pidgin English in West Africa are claimed to be interintelligible; all are primarily spoken forms, and there are but few native speakers of it (especially of Krio in Sierra Leone, and of some pidgins in Nigeria and Cameroon – but the question of what is the native or first language of a child is not always easy to decide, and of doubtful linguistic consequence in such multilingual societies).

The two West African translations are – apart from the attraction of seeing two related creoles side by side – interesting to compare: a European's feeling for the original metre is clearly evident in L. Todd's C version, which nicely illustrates what *can* be achieved in this regard. But F. Jones' text is probably closer to what is usual in the rhythmic patterns of West African languages.

K   *Krio:* Maks ɛn Mɔris by Freddie Jones

The roots of modern Krio are manifold. Clearly different from neighbouring varieties of Pidgin English (also spoken in Sierra Leone), Krio appears to have developed after the foundation of Freetown in 1787 from a fusion of coastal pidgin with the speech of newly arriving settlers, among them ex-slaves from Britain (1787), some 1100 from Nova Scotia (1792), some 550 Jamaican maroons (1800) and thousands of recaptives, taken by the

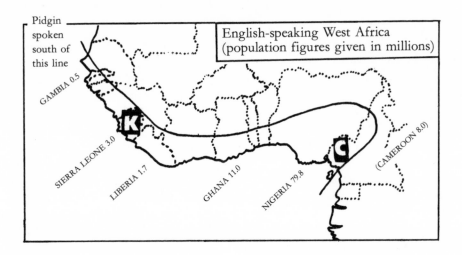

Pidgin spoken south of this line

English-speaking West Africa (population figures given in millions)

GAMBIA 0.5
SIERRA LEONE 3.0
LIBERIA 1.7
GHANA 11.0
NIGERIA 79.8
(CAMEROON 8.0)

British from slave traders of various nationalities (1808–54). Although their numbers were frequently decimated by diseases, French attacks and by re-migration, the various components seem to have led to a unique creolization product: since the language was of higher prestige than neighbouring indigenous languages, it was creolized quite early, and spread as a lingua franca through the country. All this has not, however, led to full acceptability: British English is still the language of high prestige, and dominant in all written functions, in administration, the law, the schools and – largely – the media. It is significant that there has been no printed Krio Bible so far, and that the *Krio-English Dictionary* (1980) is a scholarly book which is not likely to be very influential inside the country.

Various features make F. Jones' translation a special tour de force: the cultural distance between the source and the translation is enormous, and not only is rhyme and regular metre quite unusual in Krio – which as a tone language relies on quite different rhythmical patterns, but F. Jones had to feel his way into the patterns of a very strange language – 19th-century German. His (and the Cameroon and Tok Pisin versions) do of course present very great problems of understanding for the non-initiated reader. As the glossary makes clear, it is not the great number of words from African sources, but the identification of etymologically English words whose pronunciation was adapted to African language patterns – and of course the divergent syntax. The orthography here used is taken from Fyle/Jones, the one likely to be accepted not only for Krio but for all forms of pidgin in West Africa.

Freddie Jones was born in 1943 in Freetown, Sierra Leone; he is a native speaker of Krio. After his studies at Fourah Bay College (1962–66) he took an M.A. in Linguistics and English Language Teaching at Leeds (1972), returned to teach English in Sierra Leone (1975–80), since when he completed his Ph.D. on "English words in Krio" (Leeds, 1983). He was one of the editorial assistants for Fyle/Jones (1980).

Literature:

Fyle, Clifford N./Eldred D. Jones, *A Krio-English Dictionary*. Oxford: UP, and Free-town: Sierra Leone UP, 1980.

Spencer, John, ed., *The English Language in West Africa*. London: Longman, 1971.

Todd, Loreto, "The English language in West Africa", in Bailey/Görlach 1982:281–305.

C   *Cameroon Pidgin:* Tar an Tava by Loreto Todd

Cameroon is unique among African states in having, for 8–9 million inhabitants, not only two European languages as national languages, but in addition some 300 indigenous languages – and pidgin, which here reaches its easternmost point in West Africa. Pidgin must have been established from the 17–18th century, but it became more widespread and expanded functionally with the coming of the missionaries and German colonial rule in the late 19th century. Despite its low prestige among upper class Cameroonians, and its being banned from schools, it still serves a vital function as a lingua franca in the western part of the country and, to some extent, in the bigger towns elsewhere – the multilingua-lism of the country crying out for such a means of communication. Structurally, the language is clearly a dialect of the West African pidgin continuum; its divergences lie in some lexical items and uses. It is claimed that the language is inter-intelligible with all other forms of West African pidgin, including Krio.

Cameroon pidgin, like all West African languages, has no tradition of rhymed or metrical poetry. L. Todd's (and F. Jones') attempts are therefore daring but nonetheless successful. The C text was tested on native speakers of Cameroonian who loved the text and also suggested minor improvements. As regards contents, the simple story is surprisingly easy to 'Africanize': this involves the introduction of local names, local comparisons, dishes, dress and customs – and pidgin proverbs –, but also the fact that the teacher prefers pidgin; yet the baker – a newly important European profession – takes pride in his 'propa English'.

Loreto Todd (for whose full biography see above, I) has an intimate knowledge of Cameroon and pidgin, which date back to her four years' stay in the country. Since then, she has repeatedly revisited the Cameroons, though for shorter periods. For *Tar an Tava,* her first text in Cameroon Pidgin, she would like to acknowledge the helpful suggestions of Kenjo Jumbam and Ezekiel Vivansi.

Literature:

Todd, Loreto, *Some Day Been Dey*. West African Pidgin Folktales. London: Routledge, 1979.

–, *Cameroon*. (Varieties of English around the World). Heidelberg: Groos, 1982.

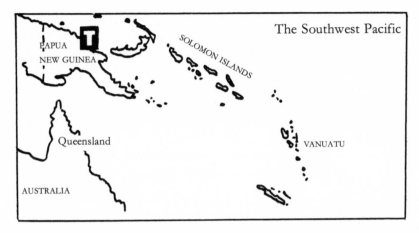

The Southwest Pacific

PAPUA NEW GUINEA

SOLOMON ISLANDS

Queensland

VANUATU

AUSTRALIA

T *New Guinea Tok Pisin:* Max na Moritz by Don Laycock

The southwest Pacific is linguistically one of the most heterogeneous areas in the world. An estimated 750 different languages in Papua New Guinea (population: 2.5 million) alone testify to this complexity; but their number also indicates why pidgins had such an excellent chance of being accepted as lingua francas. The history of Tok Pisin, of Solomon Pijin, and of Bislama in Vanuatu, and their cognates on the Australian mainland is all the more impressive because these languages have developed in the course of the last hundred years, and language expansion, standardization and planning, language shift and language death are all happening with great rapidity before our eyes, presenting us with a situation which has been aptly called a "sociolinguistic laboratory" (Wurm 1979).

The origins of these pidgins lie in the 19th-century whalers' and sandalwooders' jargon – somehow related to a Chinese-Pacific pidgin – which stabilized on plantations in Samoa (Mühlhäusler 1982), and later in Queensland, and was then transplanted with returning labourers to New Guinea, the Solomons and New Hebrides. When Tok Pisin spread under the German colonial administration, which was neutral to the new lingua franca, it was left alone to develop far away from its lexifier language, viz. English; its grammar was basically complete by the turn of the century. The story is quite different in the Papuan south, where 'broken English' was discredited and its function largely filled by Motu – or 'proper English' – by the Australian administrators. After independence, the pidgins had less of the stigma of colonial languages than pidgins elsewhere, and Tok Pisin, Solomon Pijin and Bislama are accordingly the only English-based pidgins (with incipient creolization) that have achieved national recognition: Tok Pisin fulfils many of the functions of a standard language in Papua New Guinea, and Vanuatu is said to be the only nation in the world to have its constitution printed in an English-based pidgin (Bislama).

Most writing in Tok Pisin has been in prose (instructional and educational), but there has been some creative writing, including poetry and songs (Laycock 1977). Tok Pisin has, however, no tradition of rhymed verse, and Don Laycock's achievement is therefore all the more remarkable – many would have even doubted that there were enough rhyming words available for a text of this length. The translation has been tested, with great success, on Papua New Guinean children in both towns and villages.

Donald C. Laycock was born in 1936 in Newcastle, N.S.W., Australia, and after studying modern languages there, he took his Ph.D. in the Research School of Pacific Studies, ANU Canberra, with a dissertation on a group of languages of the Sepik area of Papua New Guinea. After two years of lecturing in the United States and travelling in Europe and North Africa, he rejoined the Australian National University in 1964 as a staff member, devoting his time to languages of Papua New Guinea and the Solomon Islands. Much of his research has been on forms and functions of Tok Pisin, on which he has written extensively.

It was planned to include at least a section of *Max and Moritz* in a Bislama translation, but my attempts to commission one have come to nothing.

Literature:

Laycock, D. C., "Pidgin English in New Guinea", in: W. S. Ramson, ed., *English Transported: Essays on Australasian English.* Canberra: ANU Press, 1970, pp. 102–22.

–, "Creative writing in New Guinea Pidgin", in S. A. Wurm, ed., *Language, Culture, Society and the Modern World.* Canberra: Pacific Linguistics, 1977, pp. 609–38.

Mihalic, F., *The Jacaranda Dictionary and Grammar of Melanesian Pidgin.* Milton, Qld.: Jacaranda, ²1971.

Mühlhäusler, Peter, *Growth and Structure of the Lexicon of New Guinea Pidgin.* Canberra: Pacific Linguistics, 1979.

–, "Tok Pisin in Papua New Guinea", in Bailey/Görlach 1982: 439–66.

Wurm, S. A., ed., *New Guinea and Neighboring Areas: A Sociolinguistic Laboratory.* The Hague: Mouton, 1979.

–, et al., *Handbook of New Guinea Pidgin.* Canberra: Pacific Linguistics, 1985.

O   *Old English:* Mac ond Mauris by Manfred Görlach

M   *Middle English:* Mak and Morris by Manfred Görlach

Translations into 'dead' languages are always problematic (much more so than vice versa) – although many people would distinguish between translations into Latin and Greek (legitimate) and other languages (exotic and eccentric). Whereas it can rightly be claimed that the full linguistic potential of a language becomes available only through its active use (and this is true for living and dead languages), the awkward difference is that for dead languages there are no judges to say whether the result is acceptable, or would have been to contemporary ears. There are some additional problems that pose themselves here more clearly than in other translations (cf. Görlach 1986):

1. Must a translator use a literary form or tradition known to have been used, or can he freely use the form of his original, *Max und Moritz?*
2. Should the translator be content with words recorded in dictionaries, or can he invent words?
3. Should the translator medievalize the content of the story as well as the language?

4. Is it legitimate for him to use allusions and quotations from original poetry and thus add mock-seriousness and travesty?

5. Should he go further and 'prove' that the translation is in fact old?

In my three versions in older forms of the English language I have attempted all possible solutions:

My Old English *Maccus and Mauris* (1977, 1979) is in alliterative long lines, the usual form for Old English poetry. This has made it possible to insert original lines (from quite different heroic contexts); some of the attraction of such a pastiche is probably the delight in identifying *Maccus* lines as coming from *Beowulf* etc., and then realizing how strangely adequate they are in the new context.

Here is a passage transferring the gloom and horror of Grendel's approach to Heorot to the beetles' march towards Uncle's nose, followed by a classical battle-scene in the style of *Beowulf, Maldon, Elene* and *Exodus,* all ransacked for phrases or complete lines (= *Maccus* 229–54, roughly equivalent to *Mac* 317–30). The difference in line numbers alone makes it clear that *Maccus* is a free paraphrase rather than a translation; note some verbal reminiscences in the later rhymed version.

     Ac bitolan of pylwe   bysige uteodon,
230 scaduhelma gesceapu   scriðan comon,
     wan under wolcnum,   werod unfæger.
     La, brunbyrnedra sum,   budda fyrmest,
     nydwracu niþgrim   nihtbealwa mæst
     nebb Freoðurices,   nose gelahte.
235 "Hwæt, helle hæfta"   hrimde se eam,
     Mid egesan gedrefed   efstode fram bedde
     and fyrmestum bitolan   to banan wearð,
     oþerum, þriddan,   on earme and scancan
     creopende untydre,   crudende and fleogende,
240 hearde herebitolan,   hilde grædige,
     fage feondscaðe;   ac fæste hæfde
     grim on grape   guðbitolena unrim,
     ne hiera lifdagas   leoda ænigum
     nytte tealde.   Nietenu wiston
245 þæt hiera ealdres   wæs ende gegongen
     dogera dægrim,   deaþfæge wæron:
     Biter wæs se beaduræs;   bitolan crungon
     on gehwæðere handa,   hyssas lagon,
     niþgrime nihtscuwan.   No ic on niht gefrægn
250 under heofones hwealfe   heardran feohtan,
     hildegesan maran.   Hræfn weorces gefeah,
     urigfeðre earn   sið beheold
     wælhreowes wig.   Wulf sang ahof,
     atol æfenleoð   ætes on wenan.

The otherwise inevitable anachronisms are avoided by the invention of a pseudohistoric story of emigrant speakers of Old English having preserved their language in N Germany until after 1865; they – not the translator – had developed their lexicon by creative new formations for modern concepts such as *Tabakspfeife, Flintenpulver* etc.; they – not the editor – are responsible for corruptions of the old heroic metre.

My Old English *Mac and Mauris* (December 1982, and here printed for the first time) imposes Busch's metre and rhymescheme on Old English diction, and apart from some medievalization (partly taken over from my earlier version) is an attempt to *translate* the text; in particular, I have tried to combine rhyme with an irregular and subsidiary use of alliteration. Since, however, Old English poetic formulas have been used where appropriate (many do not scan and cannot be employed), the translation is 'free'. Gaps in the transmission of OE texts, and in our knowledge of OE poetry in general, at least make it possible to reconstruct a hypothetical textual history, following the indication of the subtitle that the poem was translated on English soil from the Old Saxon, by an Old Saxon monk, who came across the Channel ca. 884 together with John, called by King Alfred to rebuild the educational system after Scandinavian raids. Anachronisms are, in consequence, passed over as well as possible. (A minor joke is that Bauer Mecke's Low German is rendered by a fictitious 'Anglemangle', a broad 10th-century Lincolnshire mixture of Scandinavian and Old Anglian).

Various colleagues read the translation in draft form and made valuable suggestions; I am especially grateful to Jane Roberts, Franz Wenisch and Marianne Zuleger.

Decisions were much easier for the Middle English (1981) *Mak and Morris*. The English verse by Chaucer, or in the Chaucer tradition, provides not only the regular metre and rhymepairs, but also – at least with Chaucer himself – the succinctly witty self-contained couplet, often of a proverbial character, which appears to be much closer to Busch than most other literature written at a later date (the existence of a great number of inflectional syllables in 15th-century English is also a great help). Accordingly, I have tried a more thorough medievalization (with some mock quotations) than in the two Old English versions, e.g. in the opening and end pieces in which the minstrel addresses his audience; in the christianization throughout (the hens seen as martyrs, rising from purgatory etc.); in Bolte's garbled Latin; in the translator's end-piece asking God's grace and forgiveness. All this is not a necessary procedure for a translator: Rien van den Broek's Middle High German one is, in fact, much closer to Busch, and is even closer than many modern dialect translations (in Görlach 1982a). Note that even for Mecke a Chaucerian model was available: just as the two students converse in Yorkshire dialect in the *Reeve's Tale,* Black uses a distinctly Northern dialect in *Mak and Morris*. Again, the translator can pose as the lucky finder of the original 15th-century manuscript, who, as the editor of the poem, is obliged to print it letter by letter – errors and all.

The text is here reprinted from *The gestes of Mak and Morris, very critically edited...* (Heidelberg: Winter, 1981), which contains a full introduction and notes; the publisher's consent to reprint the poem is gratefully acknowledged.

Literature

Clark Hall, John R., *A Concise Anglo-Saxon Dictionary*. Cambridge: UP, [4]1969.

Davis, Norman, *et al., A Chaucer Glossary*. Oxford: Clarendon, 1979.

Görlach, Manfred, "Versuch über die Möglichkeit, *Max und Moritz* ins Altenglische zu übersetzen", *Wilhelm-Busch-Jahrbuch* 1978: 83f.

–, "Diachronic translation, or, Old and Middle English revisited", *Studia Anglica Posnaniensia* 18 (1986).

Pearsall, Derek, *Old and Middle English Poetry*. London: Routledge, 1977.

Weimann, Klaus,*Einführung ins Altenglische*. Heidelberg: Quelle & Meyer, 1982.

Manfred Görlach was born in 1937 in Berlin. He grew up in Lower Saxony, studied in Berlin, Durham, Heidelberg and Oxford (Ph. D. Heidelberg 1970). He taught Medieval Studies and English Linguistics in the English Department of Heidelberg University from 1967 to 1984, when he took up a Chair of English at the University of Cologne. He has published various books on medieval literature, English language history – and *Max und Moritz,* and has been the editor of Middle English Texts; English World-Wide; Varieties of English around the World; and a handbook (together with R. W. Bailey) *English as a World Language* (1982). He has been married since 1971; his two boys Tobias and Benjamin are of Max and Moritz' age (ten and eight) – and Benjamin happens to share his birthday with Wilhelm Busch.

Middle Scots: Mak and Moreis by Hans H. Meier

This ingenious version was translated in May/June 1984, and it was owing to a delay in the production of the book that I was fortunate enough to include it here. Hans Meier keeps very close to Wilhelm Busch's text – without giving away the fiction that the poem is late medieval. The excellence of his translation, apparently aided by the rich vocabulary and wit of the literary tradition of 16th-century Scots, is borne out by solutions for notoriously difficult lines, such as the mock stiltedness of

191f. Mairatour, als thairanent,
    Sic thing geiffis nane eisament,

or the enjambement (*Mai-/Käfer*) in

303f. Ilk ane wate: ane littill clok-
    Chafer is na thrissill cok.

Hans H. Meier was born at Zürich in 1924, where he took his doctorate in English and German philology in 1952 with a dissertation on Middle English syntax. He worked for the Dictionary of the Older Scottish Tongue from 1955 to 1959; this and the fact that he is the author of a very successful translation (into German) of Milton's *Paradise Lost* (Reclam edition) will make it easier to understand the high quality of his M&M version which combines textual faithfulness to the original with idiomatic wit and an easy flow of the lines. Since 1963, Hans H. Meier has been professor of English at the Free University of Amsterdam, where he is a colleague of Rien van den Broek, the translator of the story into Middle High German.

MAX UND MORITZ

Eine Bubengeschichte
in
sieben Streichen

Hochdeutsche
Originalfassung

MAC AND MURRAY

A Tale of Two Rascals
in Seven Episodes

translated by
Elly Miller

MEYK AN MOAS

A tyale o twee bad lads an
thor sivvin skeylaaks,
telt iv aad-fashint Mid-Northumbrian
varse by Roland Bibby.

MACK AN MAURICE

A shannakh for childher in seven cracks
torned intil Irish
be A.N. Seymour an Loreto Todd

DOD AND DAVIE

A tale of twa laddies
in seiven ploys
owreset intil Scots
be J. K. Annand

MATT AN MALKIE

A story aboot two boays in sivven terrs
translaitit intae Glesga dialeck
bi Stephen Mulrine

MAC AN MATTHY

A speil aboot twaa royit loonies
in seiven pliskies,
translated into Northeastern Scots
by J. Derrick McClure.

JARM AN JEEMSIE

A tale o twa reebalds in seevin pairts
owreset til Shetlandic
bi Derick Herning

MAX UND MORITZ

Vorwort

Ach, was muß man oft von bösen
Kindern hören oder lesen!!
Wie zum Beispiel hier von diesen,

Welche Max und Moritz hießen;
5 Die, anstatt durch weise Lehren
Sich zum Guten zu bekehren,
Oftmals noch darüber lachten
Und sich heimlich lustig machten. –

MAC AND MURRAY

Prologue

Think how frequently one reads
of some youngsters' wicked deeds.
Take for instance Mac and Murray
who caused pain and harm and worry;
5 who instead of being good,
doing everything they should,
mocked at kindness, laughed at virtue,
only practised what might hurt you. –

MEYK AN MOAS

THE FOORWARD

Ee, sic tyales – nee ward uv a lee!
Tyales o baiorns thit's wickid, hwee,
kennin bettor than thor daas,
mock at hyamely wisdim's saas,
5 swaapin monny a wink an gaiorn.
Mischif's aal thi ivvor laiorn.
Sic a paior waas Meyk an Moas,
arly weaned as mankeynd's foas;

MACK AN MAURICE

FIRNENST

We've heard tell or seen it writ
o weeans that nivir diz their bit,
lek these baygles Mack and Maurice
see their thrahin in these stories.
5 Far from thryin to mik their sowl
wʌdn't do what they was towl;
wʌdn't lissen till their betthers –
what kin you expect from ketthers?

DOD AND DAVIE

FOREWORD

What for maun we thole wee laddies
when they are sic awfu baddies!
For ensample let me save ye
frae a pair like Dod and Davie,
5 wha insteid o tryin harder
to be guid lads, get nae farder;
slee wee deils, they smirk and snicker,
lauchin gars their badness siccar.

MATT AN MALKIE

FOREWURD

Haw, the wickit things weans dae,
ye read ur hear aboot, lik say
fir instince these two, ay –
Matt an Malkie, as thur cried.
5 Well, insteid a daein right,
they wur bad, jist oota spite.
They'd nae time fur Moral Books,
sniggered it thum up thur jouks;

MAC AN MATTHY

PROLOG

Losh! Foo aft we hears or reads
tales o royit loonies' deeds!
Jist lik iss twaa nickums bad:
Mac an Matthy's fit ey're caad.
5 Steid o livin douce an genty,
takin heed o wysins tenty,
ey wad seener laach an snirt,
turnin rede tae hidlin chirt.

JARM AN JEEMSIE

WIRD AFORE

Nooadays der mony boys
taen till fir der weekit ploys!
Laek dis twa here, be me feth,
Jarm an Jeemsie, oolets baith.
5 Döin weel an lear dey haetit,
idders' wirds dey nivver leetit,
bit dey skirl an laach laek donkeys,
smeege, whin telt at dey ir monkeys.

– Ja, zur Übeltätigkeit,
10 Ja, dazu ist man bereit! –
– Menschen necken, Tiere quälen,
Äpfel, Birnen, Zwetschen stehlen – –
Das ist freilich angenehmer
Und dazu auch viel bequemer,
15 Als in Kirche oder Schule
Festzusitzen auf dem Stuhle. –
– Aber wehe, wehe, wehe!
Wenn ich auf das Ende sehe!! –

– Ach, das war ein schlimmes Ding,
20 Wie es Max und Moritz ging.
– Drum ist hier, was sie getrieben,
Abgemalt und aufgeschrieben.

Yes indeed, for trick and crime
10 they would always find the time!
Making fun of people's habits,
teasing cats and dogs and rabbits,
stealing apples, pears and cherries,
pinching plums and bagging berries –
15 all seemed nicer than to stay
stuck in church or school all day. –
But beware, beware, beware
of the end of this affair!
Mac andMurray's dreadful story
20 brought them neither gain nor glory.
What they did is here related,
written down and illustrated.

vexin foaks an yows an beeists,
10 pinchin piors an plums for feeists –
easyor faar an nivvor tyul
leyke 'tis beydin still i skyul.
But the milns o God, wheyles slaa,
Greynds *irr*oond ti baiorns an aa;
15 An hwin lads shud bettor ken,
marcy's nivvor shaan – na, nyen!
Ai-di-mi, ai, dio*r*y me,
ta*rr*ibul thor end can be.
Ey, *pr*eyde cums afo*r*e a faa …
20 Sa, fa waanin, yin an aa,
hior this tyale o Meyk an Moas,
hoo thi gat a bluddied noas.

Girnin, jeerin at their masthers:
10 here's the right wee pair o plasthers!
Them's the boys cʌd act the lig –
man's not good when small or big:
Coddin sthrangers, pokin brutes,
proggin orchards, stalin fruits,
15 playactin is far more sport
nor winnin hay or dibblin dort,
or sittin still upon a stool
in the chorch or at the school.
Haul <u>yir</u> whisht for it's wile sad
20 Mack an Maurice torned ti bad.
Before wir eyes, their en was woe
as words an picthers now will show.

Ay, for deevilrie uncheckit
10 that is aye to be expeckit!
Folks they tease, gar dumb beasts squeal
aipples, peers and plooms they steal.
That's the sort of pleisand ploy
gies them far mair muckle joy
15 nor sittin quate upon a stuil
in the kirk or in the schuil.
Dear, oh dear, oh dearie dear!
Th'outcome o't is far frae clear.
'Twas a wicked road and lang
20 Dod and Davie waled to gang.
Here's the tale, as far's I kent it,
set in picturs and here prentit.

when it's durty wurk ye need,
10 here's aye wullin hauns an heid.
Turmentin people, dugs an cats,
knockin fruit, appeals tae brats;
a stolen aipple, plum, ur perr,
they think's magic – who'd prefer
15 widden sates in church ur skule?
(Thurs nuthin ye kin teach a fule.)
Bit oh dear, whit a wey tae go –
Matt an Malkie – oh, oh, oh!
Here's thur story set in haun,
20 doon oan paper, wrut an drawn.

Aye, but coorse-lik deeds tae dee,
10 fock's ay gleg, an ay wull be!
Beasts ey'd towt, an fock ey'd swick,
aipples, peirs an plooms ey'd nick.
Certie, ploys lik yon gies mair
rigs an jeists an daffins rare
15 nor tae sit i'th' Kirk at peace,
or upo the scholar's deece.
But alack, alack, alack,
fin A thinks fit gate ey'll tak!
Dool an wae it is tae ken
20 Mac an Matthy's gruesome enn.
Sae, here aa eir deeds o vrang,
vrocht in pictur an in sang.

Dey wir aaber ev'ry oor
10 fir a ploy at made fock soor.
Hattrin aald wives, leddrin baess,
raandrin taaties, neeps or peas,
dis dey truly tocht wis maddrim,
an fir dem wis far mair lichtsome
15 as ta sit in kirk or schöl
still laek stanes apo a stöl.
– Less a less an tweetishee,
whin I noo da ootcome see.
Hit wis vyld an nae doot sair,
20 foo dis tö-taks did misfare.
Sae, doo sees in wird an pent
der ill tricks, ta mak dem kent.

ERSTER STREICH

Mancher gibt sich viele Müh
Mit dem lieben Federvieh;
25 Einesteils der Eier wegen,
Welche diese Vögel legen,
Zweitens: weil man dann und wann
Einen Braten essen kann;
Drittens aber nimmt man auch
30 Ihre Federn zum Gebrauch
In die Kissen und die Pfühle,
Denn man liegt nicht gerne kühle. –

FIRST EPISODE

There are people who work hard
keeping poultry in the yard.
25 First of all because they may
eat the eggs their chickens lay.
Secondly, since now and then,
they can roast a juicy hen.
Thirdly there is further use
30 for a chicken, duck or goose,
when their warming down and feather
comforts in cold winter weather.

Seht, da ist die Witwe Bolte,
Die das auch nicht gerne wollte.

Here you see one Widow Bold
who preferred her warmth to cold.

Forst Skeylaak

Lots o canny foak, yi ken,'s
va*rr*y fond o keepin hens;
25 pullits heor an banties thior,
sum teymes fancy bords thit's dior.
Hens, forbey tho*r* eggs fo tea,
noo an then'll *r*oast, yi see;
'seyds, i fithor bed ey licks
30 flock or st*r*aa in st*r*eypy ticks.
Stuffed in pillas sheynin wheyte,
fethors help yi sleep at neyght.
Widda Boolor, she waas yin –
hyatid chilly neyghts leyke sin;

Forst Thrick

Many's a wan that hez the time
thinks rarin hens is simply prime.
25 Forst because wir brave wee fowl
lays their eggs wi'out been towl.
Then, a howl there's no debate
roasted fowl's a darlin mate.
Thordly, for a hen's or goose's
30 fe'ers there is many uses.
Dale a man that hez some fowl
need be worried o the cowl.
Wan o these wʌz Wida Kelly –
here's hir lekness. Tik a skelly.

First Ploy

Monie a wifie taks great pains
wi her precious cocks and hens;
25 first for aa the eggs they lay
for their mistress ilka day;
neist, because a bodie can
eat a roast hen nou and than;
third, the feathers come in handy
30 fillin cods and bowsters dandy;
no a bodie, sae it's said
likes to chitter in her bed.
See, there is the Weeda Bauld
finnds she canna bide the cauld.

Furst Terr

Maist folk's awful foand a hens –
cannae whack thum, it's gude sense –
furstly, cuz ye've goat the eggs,
an seckintly, roast chicken legs,
25 a blaw-oot, wance in ivry while,
thit leaves ye sittin wi a pile
a feathurs ye kin pit tae use,
tae keep yir bed an aw the hoose
warm as toast oan winter's nights –
30 sumthin ivrybuddy likes –
so quilts an pillas makes the thurd
asset goatten affa burd.
Widda Blooter thoat the same,
an cozzy that, she kep at hame,

First Pliskie

Mony fock haads muckle steir
wi eir chuckie hennies dear.
25 First, for eggies we can hae
fin the bonnie birdies lay.
Neist, we aets em nooanan,
birsselt in the skirlie pan.
Ae mair rizzon: we can tak
30 doonie fedders saft, tae pack
intae cods an cushins tee –
caalrife box-neds winna dee!
Weeda Bannock – see her here –
likes em neen ava, A'm seer.

Plunkie Wan

Mony fock ir wint ta keep
hens an deuks firby der sheep.
25 First an foremaist caas dey öse
aa da eggs dis braa fools lays.
Dan bicaas dey noo an dan
laek ta rost dem i da pan.
Fedders tö dey winna tarrow,
30 fillin wi dem twilt an pillow,
fir dey hate ta stirn wi caald
trow da nicht, baith young an aald.
Weedow Baald as weel, hit's said,
coodna dree da caald in bed.

<table>
<tr><td>

35 Ihrer Hühner waren drei
    Und ein stolzer Hahn dabei. –

    Max und Moritz dachten nun:
    Was ist hier jetzt wohl zu tun? –
    – Ganz geschwinde, eins, zwei, drei,
40 Schneiden sie sich Brot entzwei,
    In vier Teile, jedes Stück
    Wie ein kleiner Finger dick.
    Diese binden sie an Fäden,
    Übers Kreuz, ein Stück an jeden,

</td><td>

35 Chickens were her poultry stock,
    three fat hens and one proud cock.

    Mac and Murray soon began
    to devise their wicked plan.
    Quickly they procure some bread,
40 cut it up, and now some thread;
    this they lay upon the floor,
    crossed and knotted into four.
    On each end are neatly tied
    bits of bread each finger-wide.

</td></tr>
</table>

45 Und verlegen sie genau   45 All is left with care and calm,
    In den Hof der guten Frau. –   near the widow's chicken farm.

35 sa she doatid on hor flock,
    three fat hens an yin proud cock.
    "Ai!" sayd Moas, an "Ee!" sayd Meyk,
    "yon lot huz'll fettle, leyk."
    Shaap as shaap, sum crusts thi saa
40 inti fowor fingors smaa.
    Each o them iroond the wayist
    wi yi streeng-end's form imbrayist.
    Fowor streengs, thor spior ends jeyned,
    stretcht oot, breeng a cross ti meynd.
45 Beydin fa the widda's frey,
    fowor temptin maasils ley …

35 Three plump hens wʌz all hir care
    an a cock as proud as Lucifer.
    Mack an Maurice dandhered by,
    thought a thrick they'd lek ti thry.
    Wan, two, three! The two young carls
40 grabbed some heels o home-made farls.
    Cut each heel in four divides
    each a finger thick in size.
    These they tie ti criss-crossed twine
    two firnenst an two ahine,
45 set the thrap in Kelly's back
    an hide themselves ti watch the crack.

35 She'd three hens amang her stock
    as weel's a proud and handsome cock.
    Dod and Davie, sad to say
    thocht upon a ploy to play.
    In the crackin o a whup
40 get some breid and cut it up
    in fower pieces – and what think ye? –
    ilka bit as thick's my pinkie!
    Wi lenths o string they jine ilk bit,
    in shape o cross they gar them fit.
45 Skeelie hands they were that made them.
    In the guidwife's yaird they laid them.

35 apart fae three hens howkin coarn,
    a coack furby, as shure's yir boarn.
    Matt an Malkie, noo, trust them,
    stert tae play thur ain wee gemme,
    an quick as winkie, wan, two, three!
40 choap thur piece up, as ye see,
    four wee dauds a breid, sliced white,
    each the size i a chicken's bite.
    Nixt they tied thum oantae twine,
    laid croassweys, a baited line,
45 spread thum oan the Widda's grun,
    then sat back tae watch he fun.

35 She hed three wee chuckies blye,
    wi a paachtie cock forbye.
    Mac an Matthy 'gud tae think:
    "Ony chance here for a gink?"
    Een-twaa-three – wi skeely bled,
40 seen a fang o breid ey sned.
    Fower wee pickies: ilkie mannie
    naeweys braider nor yer crannie.
    Lik a cross ey wap em ower
    tae the enns o stringies fower,
45 syne the strings is featly laired
    in the gweed aal deem's back yaird.

35 Tree fat hens wis in her yaird,
    wi a cock at did dem gaird.
    Jarm an Jeemsie toucht at dis
    wis a ploy dey soodna miss.
    In a scad da reebalds cuts
40 cassen bread in minkie bits.
    Fower pairts dey shön hae clair,
    finger tick dey ir, nae mair.
    Dis dey bind ta cross-laid strings,
    at da ends da pieces hings.
45 I da göd wife's yaird dey smoot,
    peerie wyes dey set dem oot.

Kaum hat dies der Hahn gesehen,	As the bread begins to show,
Fängt er auch schon an zu krähen:	so the cockerel starts to crow:
Kikeriki! Kikikeri!! –	Cock-a-doodle-doodle-day!
50 Tak tak tak! – da kommen sie.	50 Watch them waddle down this way.

Hahn und Hühner schlucken munter,	Merrily the chickens munch
Jedes ein Stück Brot hinunter;	each a crust of bread for lunch;

Aber als sie sich besinnen,	but they realise just too late,
Konnte keines recht von hinnen.	no more can they separate.

Waatchfu cock craas, "Lasses! Baiyit!"
Cluckin hens rush up, nyen blate;
fussin, squaakin, foo o glee,
50 happy it waas teyme fo tea.
Each yin gowps a tayisty crust,
each is ti yits marras trusst
bi the wickid chowkin cords –
hwaat a fayit fo bonny bords!

When the roosther seen the cake
he crowed an crowed wi open bake:
"Cock-a-doodle-doodle-doo!"
50 Wan, two, three, the wee hens flew.
The greedy gorbs jus lost the head
quickly gobblin up the bread.
Then the poor owl dilseys saw
they wʌz banjaxed by the craw.

When the cock thir pieces saw
loudly he begoud to craw:
"Cockadoodle, cockadee!
50 Haste ye, haste ye, come and pree!"
Cock and hens wi eident greed
gobble doun a dawd o breid;
as they warsle tane wi tither
nane can twine her frae anither,

Up steps Chanticleer, aye furst,
sterts oot crawin fit tae burst:
"Coacka-doodle-doo! C'mere!" –
50 cluck, cluck, cluck, the hens appear.
Coack an hens baith chow the breid,
swally doon thur welcome feed;
tough oan them, bit, that's them stuck;
noo they cannae craw nur cluck!

Fin iss ferlie Cockie sees,
fit a scraichin craa he gies!
"Cockie-leerie-leerie-laa!"
50 "Tick-tick" – here the hens an aa.
Doon ey gowp, but thocht or rede,
ilkie een a nirl o breid.
Fin ey preive, tho, here ey finn
aff the string ey canna win

Shön da cock dis braa sicht saa,
rexed his hass, begöd ta craa:
"Cock a doo, cock cock a doo!"
50 Tuck, tuck, tuck! Dey'r comin noo.
Cock an hens, blyde tae be fed,
glaeps an kwilks der wack o bread.
Whin dey cam ta tink hit owre,
dey wir catched ill-helt, aa fowr.

55   In die Kreuz und in die Quer
      Reißen sie sich hin und her,
	55 Tearing criss-cross back and forth,
	      East and West, and South and North,

Flattern auf und in die Höh,
     Ach herrje, herrjemine!
	up they flutter, way up high –
	     me-oh-me-oh-me-oh-my!

Ach, sie bleiben an dem langen
60   Dürren Ast des Baumes hangen. –
     – Und ihr Hals wird lang und länger,
     Ihr Gesang wird bang und bänger;
	See them sadly hanging now
	60 on this spiky, barren bough.
	     Bird-song echoes terse and terser,
	     length of neck grows worse and worser.

55 Deshin tin an tuthor gaiyit
back an forrard, iv a stayit,
haad thi tug an scritch an lowp,
rive an wammil, owor-cowp,
fluttor up an – gox! d'yi see? –
60 aal thon streengs hyukt on a tree!
Noo the weyld clamjafrey dees,
as each speerit ups an flees;

55 How they pʌlled an hauled an scratched
till no good, for they wʌz catched.
By my sang, up, up they flew –
Holy God! What can they do?
On a branch now see them grapple
60 each fowl hangin by the thrappel.
Every neck gets longer still
an their scrakes get faint an shrill.

55 jinkin, joukin, fleggit, worrit,
ruggin, tuggin, back and forrit.
Flauchter up intil the air –
what a collieshangie there!
In the tree they are nou fankelt
60 hingin frae a brainch that's runkelt.
Syne ilk craig gets lang and langer,
fear-fangit sangs are melled in anger.

55 Back an furrit, roon aboot
they wrastle, bit thurs nae wey oot,
flap thur wings fur aw they try;
then the wurst bit, my oh my –
a deid branch interceps the string,
60 they four burds ur left tae hing,
slow-like, wi thur necks ootstreetched,
swansong dwindled tae a screech.

55 Up an doon ey're rinnin, ruggin,
here an yont wi fersell tuggin.
Flaffin tae the lift ey flee –
ah, alack, alackanee!
Fae a lang an gizzent boo
60 yonner hing the craiters noo,
an eir craigs is streetchin, stretchin,
an eir fleggit peeacks fleitchin.

55 Back an fore an roond dey pin,
nyiggin, in an oot dey rin.
Flaachtrin, up an up dey flee,
dear, o dear, o dearie me!
Noo apo a tree dey hing,
60 whaar dey keek an whaar dey swing,
an der craigs grew odious lang,
gluffed an scraichin töns dey sang.

Jedes legt noch schnell ein Ei,
Und dann kommt der Tod herbei. –

Each one lays an egg, and then
death it is for cock and hen!

65 Witwe Bolte, in der Kammer,
   Hört im Bette diesen Jammer;

65 Mistress Bold has heard the wailing
   and she wonders what is ailing.

danglin, stranglin, hingin saad,
last eggs layid an last craas craad ...
65 Aal this clishmaclavor's hard;
    haaf the parish owor-aad;

As they twitch an kick their legs,
lʌk! they're layin their last eggs.
65 Wida Kelly in her room
    thinks the gloe's the crack o doom.

Frichtit, three last eggs are lain –
daith comes by to claim his kain.
65 Bauldie, beddit in her chawmer
    waukens wi the fearsome yammer.

They lay wan egg, thur final act,
afore they croak, an that's a fact.
65 The Widda, thit's the chicken's mammy,
    hears aw this unseemly rammy,

Ae last eggie ilk draps swythe
or ey faa tae Daeth's fell scythe.
65 Weeda Bannock in her chaamer
    fae her box-bed hears the yammer.

Ev'ry fool an egg dan laid,
shut hits een an drappit dead.
65 Weedow Baald, aboot ta snore,
    hears in bed dis reel an splore.

Ahnungsvoll tritt sie heraus:	Out she hurries, tense with fright,
Ach, was war das für ein Graus!	goodness, what a dreadful sight!

„Fließet aus dem Aug, ihr Tränen!	"Eyes pour forth your tears of sorrow!
70 All mein Hoffen, all mein Sehnen,	70 All life's longings for the morrow –
Meines Lebens schönster Traum	sweet my dream and reverie
Hängt an diesem Apfelbaum!!"	hangs here on this apple-tree!"

wheyle the widda hoys horsel
oot the bed, wi sic a yell,
'cross the *r*um an dun the stayor,
70 gyapin gob an tossin haior,
oot the doo-or inti the yaard,
bi hor aafu panic ga*rr*ed.

Out she runs ahent their cries –
Heth! The sight near lef her eyes.
Down her chiks the tears came thrippin
70 when she seen her boards' lives slippin.
"Life's most precious dhream", says she,
"Is hangin from thon apple three!"

Worriet sair, she braves the nicht.
Wow! She sees a gruesome sicht.
"Frae my een gush out, oh tears!
70 Aa my hopes, aa my desires,
ach, my brawest dream I see
hangit frae this aipple-tree."

springs fae bed, tae see whit's brewin,
therr's her hopes completely ruined –
"Rise up, tears, and blind ma eye!
70 Ah cannae staun tae look, Ah'll die,
cuz ivrythin Ah want ur need,
oan yon aipple-tree hings deid!"

Oot she rins in dreid an fricht:
fegs, but fit a gastrous sicht!
"Flowe, ye tear-draps, fae ma ee!
70 Aa ma howps an langins tee,
life's best draem, sae braa an fair,
hingin fae the freet-tree ere!"

Foo o dreid shö spunders oot:
Vyld da sicht shö saa, nae doot.
"Weet me sheeks, ye bitter taers!
70 Less, me joys, me pretty dears,
dis me life's maist lichtsome tings,
fae yon elder-tree noo hings!"

Tiefbetrübt und sorgenschwer	Full of woe, bereft of hope
Kriegt sie jetzt das Messer her;	Mistress Bold now cuts the rope,
75 Nimmt die Toten von den Strängen,	75 takes the corpses off the tree
Daß sie so nicht länger hängen,	to relieve their misery.

Und mit stummem Trauerblick	Sadly, silent, mortified,
Kehrt sie in ihr Haus zurück. –	she turns back and steps inside.
Dieses war der erste Streich,	That concludes the first bad deed,
80 Doch der zweite folgt sogleich.	80 there are more, as you shall read.

Ai, the seyght hor glift glance meets!
Ee, the way she hools an bleats!
75 Aal hor preyde an hwopes aglay,
ruined i this wickid way ...
Doon she hacks the dowly bords,
dowf an blunkit hairt an wawds ...
"By, yon waas a clivvor gayim!"
80 laaft the lads, "Mair o the sayim!"

Fairly broke wi all her woes
for the gully knife she goes;
75 cuts the corps from aff the bough
hangin cowl an lifeless now,
kakes wan last time wi a growse,
then she hurries ti the house.
That's the childher's forst bad thrick –
80 but the secon follies quick.

She, in dool and sorrow-sair
taks a knife to free them there;
75 cuts the corps frae aff the string
that they micht nae langer hing.
Strucken dumb, and lookin douce,
taks her hens intil the hous.
Tellin o the first tale's dune –
80 saicont follies richt ahin.

Rale upset an greetin sore,
she cuts thum doon, the hingin four;
75 draws her knife acroass the string,
wherr thon chicken coarpses swing,
picks thum up, withoot a wurd,
an kerries in each puir deid burd.
That's the Furst Terr done, an noo –
80 foallies oan Terr Number Two.

Wechtit doon wi sorra's pressin,
oot her futtle noo she's fessen.
75 Cuts the corpies fae the string:
noo nae mair the peer breets hing.
Stoon't wi wae, nae word she says:
Ben the hoose the aal deem gaes.
Pliskie Nummer Een wes yon –
80 tae the neist we'se noo meeve on.

Foo o soarroo shö is truly,
fetches dan her keetchen tully,
75 hents da krangs doon fae da tree,
sae dey irna swingin free,
dumpeesed, wae an far fae croose,
shö gings back ita da hoose.
Plunkie wan is here abön –
80 Bit da neist een follows shön.

Zweiter Streich

Als die gute Witwe Bolte
Sich von ihrem Schmerz erholte,
Dachte sie so hin und her,
Daß es wohl das beste wär,
85 Die Verstorbnen, die hienieden
Schon so frühe abgeschieden,
Ganz im stillen und in Ehren
Gut gebraten zu verzehren. –
– Freilich war die Trauer groß,
90 Als sie nun so nackt und bloß
Abgerupft am Herde lagen,
Sie, die einst in schönen Tagen

Second Episode

Just as soon as Mistress Bold
was contented, as of old,
she decided it would be
proper and correct if she
85 took the recently deceased
and prepared them for a feast.
Naturally tears were flowing
as the oven, hot and glowing,
was made ready then and there
90 for the chickens plucked and bare.
They, who only yesterday,
happy, vital, carefree, gay,

SECIND SKEYLAAK

Yin fo coontin blessins she,
Widda Boolor mopped ho*r* ee;
thowt she shuddint luk gift meat
i the beak – she'd hev a *treat*.
85 Roastid fool wud mayik a feeist
fit fa laird or heynd or p*r*eeist –
but, i this cyase, aal fa yin,
layit diceast's *r*imainin kin.
T*r*ew, the hot tiors flaad agyain
90 hwin she eed the veectims layin,
ploatid, leyfeliss, iv a paan,
nivvor maior ti seeng at daan,

SECON THRICK

Then wir dacint wida wʌman
all hir strenth she thried ti summon,
when she foun she had come till
From the stoom that made her ill.
85 Just as soon as it wʌz dacint
thought it wʌd be right an faizant
ti ate her dear departed fowl
livin onct but now corp-cowl.
Still, her head wʌz fair asthray
90 ti see her boards' lives tʌk away,
ti see them moilly as a wire
plucked an singed firnenst the fire.

SAICONT PLOY

Weeda Bauld syne gat relief
frae her sufferin and her grief;
thocht, she did, that there and than
it wad be a wycelike plan
85 gif her umquhile bairns, nou taen
or their layin days were rin,
could be honourably treatit,
roastit, and at denner eatit.
Sad it was to see them there
90 scuddie-nakit, cauld and bare,
pookit, by the kitchen grate;
they on braw days, air and late,

SECKINT TERR

Wance the Widda dried her eyes,
readers wullnae be surprised
tae hear she took a wise decision,
tae make the best i her position,
85 an eat the victums i thon crime,
cut aff in thur chicken prime,
nicely roastit, dished up neat –
a private service, like, discreet.
Mind ye, she wis stull upset;
90 it broke her hert tae see her pets
stretched oot nakit bi the grate,
scuddy feathurless, a state

SAICONT PLISKIE

Gweed aal Weeda Bannock syne
cowerit aa her hertscaad's pyne,
an a canny think hed she
fit the best thing wes tae dee.
85 Yon peer breets at weird did harl
faar ower seen fae iss dreich warl,
she, respecfu, douce an quaet,
noo wad finely rost an aet.
Weel A wat, 't wes muckle wae
90 fin ey, pluck't an nyaakit, lay
on the herth-steen aa thegidder –
ey at eence, in simmer widder,

PLUNKIE TWA

Whin pör weedow Baald neist day
wis in a far better lay,
shör begöd ta tink noo tö
at da best ting shö cood dö
85 wis ta rost an dan ta aet,
wi a soch, bit no owre blate,
dis pör fools at swack an young
jöst dastreen in dead-traa hung.
Still an on shö stöd an gret
90 whin da pluckin shö did whet
an shö saa dem lyin bare,
dis her jewels at aa dis year

Bald im Hofe, bald im Garten
Lebensfroh im Sande scharrten. –

ran about the farm-yard, and
scraped among the garden sand.

95 Ach, Frau Bolte weint aufs neu,
Und der Spitz steht auch dabei.

95 Yes – once more she has to weep!
Who looks on? – Her dog named Sweep.

Max und Moritz rochen dieses;
„Schnell aufs Dach gekrochen!" hieß es.

Mac and Murray smelt the cooking,
climbed up high and started looking

Durch den Schornstein mit Vergnügen
100 Sehen sie die Hühner liegen,

Die schon ohne Kopf und Gurgeln
Lieblich in der Pfanne schmurgeln. –

down the chimney-stack below;
100 saw the chickens in a row,

lying headless, crisp in batter,
sizzling gaily on the platter.

nivvor maior wi skeell ti staalk
haiory oubit, wawm an maak,
95 nivvor maior ti *p*rance an *p*reen
aboot the hyamely back-yaard scene ...
Noo, the lads syun nebbed yon meal,
speeled the *r*uf an stack as weel,
keeked doon i the chimbley *b*raid,
100 saa the seezlin bords deesplayed,
gleesnin, *c*racklin, *r*ich an *b*roon,
fit ti be a banquit's *c*roon!

Boards that onct went hokin, pickin
roun the yard lek any chicken.
95 Agane the wida keened an cried;
Rover gowled there at her side.
The baygles got wan whiff o roast:
"We'll clime the roof if it's not bost!"
Down the chimley pots they're kakin
100 see the wida's threasures bakin,
dhressed an on the skillet lyin
sizzlin, roastin, bubblin, fryin.

in yaird and gairden, hour by hour,
scartit happy in the stour.
95 Bauldie grat saut tears yince mair;
Dug sat waitin on the flair.
Reek o cookin, laddies smell.
"Sclim up on the ruif!" they yell.
Sune they're keekin doun the lum
100 whence grand-reekin vapours come;
see the hens there lyin, pookit,
sizzlin in the pan, near-cookit.

gey unlike thur foarmer life,
as faivrit burds i thon auld wife,
95 peckin coarn among the saun,
oan hoat days eatin oot her haun,
fulla beans an fulla grain –
noo she sterts tae greet again!
(Gyp, her wee dug, hit jines in).
100 Matt an Malkie, bit, get wind,
think, "Right, the roof!", an doon the lum
they spy the chickens, near owrecome

in an oot the hoose gaed dartin,
cheerie 'mo the chingles scartin.
95 Fegs, the Weeda grat eence mair,
Bats the doggie staanin ere.
Fin the yoam the nackets finn,
"Gleg up tae the reef we'se win!"
Goamin doon the lum, ey're blye,
100 Ere ey see the hennies lie,
Heidless, sotterin awa,
in the skellet – fittan braa!

i da yaird or on her laand
soucht fir scobbins i da saand.
95 Yea, da weedow gowled eence mair
while her hund wis staandin der.
Jarm an Jeemsie feel da waff.
"Up apo da röf!" dey gaff.
Trow da lum dey staand an glinder,
100 scrime da fools aa laid oot yunder,
fir athoot da head an gözren
i da pan dey lie der sizzlin.

Eben geht mit einem Teller
Witwe Bolte in den Keller,

Plate in hand walks Mistress Bold
to the cellar, where it's cold.

105 Daß sie von dem Sauerkohle
     Eine Portion sich hole,
     Wofür sie besonders schwärmt,
     Wenn er wieder aufgewärmt. –

     – Unterdessen auf dem Dache
110 Ist man tätig bei der Sache.
     Max hat schon mit Vorbedacht
     Eine Angel mitgebracht. –

105 Here you see her just about
     to collect her sauerkraut.
     It's a dish she likes a lot,
     most of all when served up hot.

     On the roof the boys, meanwhile,
110 villainously work their guile.
     Mac has scored with forethought here,
     he has brought his fishing-gear.

Noo the widda had a meynd
sum hoorse-radish saace ti feynd,
105 'caas she luvved the speycy tayist –
forbey, she thowt it treemed hor wayist!
Aff she tiv 'or cellor wheyle,
oworheed, the scoondrils smeyle.
Meyk, yi see, hes browt alang
110 hyuk an feeshin leyne sa strang –
just i cyase it meyght cum in
handy, like, ti forthor sin.

Down the cellar went wir wʌman
nivir thinkin what wʌz comin,
105 lʌkin out some corly cale
ti kitchen up a tasty male.
She loved corly any time,
hated up she thought it prime.
On the roof the cubs biz ap
110 busy settin up their thrap.
Roasted mate is on their mine,
so Mack has tʌk his fishin line.

Weeda Bauld gaed doun the stair
seekin kitchen til her fare;
105 ashet sune was piled wi heaps
o gowden creamy champit neeps.
Neeps left owre she never wasted –
sweirs het-up they're better tasted.
On the ruif lads taikle neist
110 weys o gettin at the feast.
Dod wi foresicht unco fine
brocht wi him a rod and line.

tae see they burds, less heids an feet,
already sparkin owre the heat.
105 Leave them turnin nicely broon,
the Widda takes an ashet doon,
tae get some peas-brose oot the dunny,
warmed wi chicken, sweet as honey.
Roon the lum, bit, owre her heid,
110 how's this fur a durty deed?
Matt, thit's whit ye'd cry a thinker,
unwraps rod, hook, line, an sinker –

tae the cellar doon the stair,
105 wi an ashet, for tae wale
oot a drappie saatit kail.
O iss maet she's byous fain
fin it's cweelt an het again.
On the reef, tho: fit's up here,
110 aa iss timmerin an mineer?
Mac's the loon tae hae his thocht:
See the fishin-wann he's brocht.

Wi a trunsher an a spön
doon da stair da wife gings shön,
105 fir ta hent a coarn o kail,
lyin wöshen in a pail.
Dis shö laeks ta oil an aet,
aft wi idder kirsen maet.
Bi da lum dey waitna lang,
110 wi der ploy dey shön ir trang.
Jarm da reebald in his haand
eence a errant broucht a waand.

Schnupdiwup! da wird nach oben
Schon ein Huhn heraufgehoben.
115 Schnupdiwup! jetzt Numro zwei;
Schnupdiwup! jetzt Numro drei;
Und jetzt kommt noch Numro vier:
Schnupdiwup! dich haben wir!! –
– Zwar der Spitz sah es genau,
120 Und er bellt: Rawau! Rawau!

Whoops! They're really having fun!
Here goes chicken number one.
115 Whoops! now two, and whoops! now three –
up they come now, hee, hee, hee!
Whoops! and up comes number four
that's the lot, there are no more.
Sweep the dog has seen it all –
120 bow-wow! is his plaintive call.

Doon it deyves, then up wi caior,
wi the forst bord hingin theor;
115 syun the next yin, an the thord;
last uv aal, the husbind bord,
*r*eyghtly *b*reengin up the *r*eor,
wance ee'd seen ees lassies cleeor.
Aal this teyme, the widda's teyke,
120 Toshor, guv the theek a heyke,

There it goes! Am talkin thrue:
Wan hen bizzin up the flue.
115 Yuch! Here comes the secon board!
Yuch! An now here comes the thord!
Number four the line hez got –
God! The hallions hez the lot!
Rover's gawkin sure enough;
120 all that he can say is: "Wuff!"

Eentie, teentie, haligolum
roastit hen flees up the lum.
115 Ticketie tacketie nummer twa,
thickerie thackerie three awa,
fitherie fetherie nummer fower –
that's the tally safely owre.
Up the lum Dug saw them gang.
120 "Bowf-wowf! Bowf-wowf!" his warnin rang.

Wheech! up comes hen number wan,
an wheech again! right oot the pan;
115 number three an four they've goat,
fisht thum up, the hale damn loat!
Up the lum four chickens flies –
puir Gyp cannae trust his eyes,
an sterts tae bark – grrwoof! grrwoof! –
120 while they dreep doon aff the roof.

Hoopsie-dosie – wi a tug,
tae the reef a hen ey drug.
115 Hoopsie-dosie – nummer twaa!
Hoopsie-dosie three an aa!
In the pan the fowert een coors:
Hoopsie-dosie – an he's oors!
Battie sees it – he's nae dowf.
120 Lood he howls wi yaff an yowf.

Haal her up! Up trow da lum
see a fine fat fool noo come.
115 Haal her up! Dere's number twa!
Haal her up! Der tree awa!
Trow da lum comes number fowr.
Haal her up! Der nane left owre!
Noo da hund der ill trick saa
120 an he yalks "Raa-waa, raa-waa!"

Aber schon sind sie ganz munter
Fort und von dem Dach herunter. –

– Na! Das wird Spektakel geben,
Denn Frau Bolte kommt soeben:
125 Angewurzelt stand sie da,
Als sie nach der Pfanne sah.

But the boys with glee and cunning,
snatch their prize and quick, start running.

Dear oh dear, 'tis as we feared!
Mistress Bold has just appeared,
125 stands there rooted to the spot
as she glances at her pot.

Alle Hühner waren fort –
„Spitz!!" – das war ihr erstes Wort. –

All her lovely chickens gone!
Sweep is whom she seizes on.

„Oh, du Spitz, du Ungetüm!! –
130 Aber wart! ich komme ihm!!!"

"Sweep, you fiend, you reprobate!
130 I shall get you – just you wait!"

till horsel cum pantin back,
wheyle the lads fleed aff the stack.
She waas flabborgastid, man,
hwen she saa the empty pan –
125 staatled, scumfished, moidart, gliffed –
Marcy! Wes hor meynd adrift?
Na! It had ti be yon hoond!
Waatch-dog, meynd – gud job, aal foond!
"TOSHOR! Greet fond bowdikeyte!
130 Aa'll larn ye hwaat's wrang, hwaat's reyght!"

Thon two skitthers lep away
light their load for they wʌz gay.
Heth there'll be a ragin row –
Wida Kelly's comin now!
125 There she stʌd wi open gob
when she seen the empy hob.
"Where's me fowl?" she lets wan yelp
an started in ti bate an skelp.
"Yi dorty atin gorb! Yi brute!
130 I'll get at yi wi me boot!"

Dod and Davie arena blate.
Aff the ruif they tak the gate.
What a stishie there was when
Mistress Bauld cam toddlin ben.
125 Fair dumfounert, tae, at that,
when she lookit at the pat.
Aa her roastit hens awa!
Syne her puir wee Dug she saw.
"Dug!" she yelled, "ye ill-faured gett ye!
130 Juist you wait until I get ye."

Wait the noo, though, whit's this comin?
Who's this back? The widda-wumman!
She sees burds vamoosed, the loat,
stauns therr, rootit tae the spoat;
125 the pan's strippt shameless, nut a burd,
an "Gyp!" uv coorse, that's the wurd.
"Gyp!" she cries, "Ya greedy messan!"
"By Goad, this time learn yir lesson!"

But, for aa the doggie's yelpin,
doon ey speil, an aff ey're skelpin!
Losh, but noo we'se see some steir:
Eence again the Weeda's here!
125 'Stonisht, staanin lik a stookie,
fin o th' pan she taks a leukie.
Ne'er a hennie ere tae seek.
"Battie!" wes her foremaist speak.
"Bats, ye gutsy little tyke!
130 Ye're the een A'm gyaan tae pyke!"

Bit dey'r clum doon fae da röf
Wi dis braa proil i der löf.
Yea, dey'll shön be hubbleskyoo,
fir da weedow's comin noo.
125 Shö ständ dere dumfoondered an
trimmlin whin shö saa da pan.
Aa da fools is clean awa
an her een on hund dan faa.
"Condwined hund, ill sunse on dee!
130 Jöst doo wait, A'll mak dee swee!"

Mit dem Löffel, groß und schwer,
Geht es über Spitzen her;
Laut ertönt sein Wehgeschrei,
Denn er fühlt sich schuldenfrei. –

With the ladle on his back,
sweep is under fierce attack.
Loudly do his cries proclaim
he is not the one to blame.

135 –Max und Moritz, im Verstecke,
Schnarchen aber an der Hecke,
Und vom ganzen Hühnerschmaus
Guckt nur noch ein Bein heraus. –

Dieses war der zweite Streich,
140 Doch der dritte folgt sogleich.

135 In the bushes, Mac and Murray
sleep contented, in no hurry.
What a sumptuous feed it's been!
Only drum-sticks can be seen.

That's the second wicked deed –
140 there are more, as you shall read.

Ivry ward she says she brays
Toshor in myaist pyainfu ways
wi a muckle sarvin spiun,
hweyle ee hools the hwole hoose diun ...
135 Meyk un Mose injeyd thor bayit;
aal but yin leg syun thi'd aiyit.
Hint the hedge thi smorked an snaad,
Teyme the widda scritched an raad.
"Seccind vic'try!" creyd wor paior,
140 "but the thord yin'll be raior!"

Grabs a ladle quick an "Thump"
down it comes on Rover's rump.
Rover's howls wʌd cut yir ear –
he knows well he's conscience-clear.
135 Mack an Maurice, fʌll as shʌkhs
snore an sleep beneath a bʌsh;
from the fowl that they had nyʌkht
ony wan wee leg is lʌkt.
That's the gʌlpins' secon thrick –
140 Number three will folly quick.

Wi her muckle ladle skelpit
at her puir wee Dug that yelpit
loud at ilka dunt and dang –
puir bruit felt he'd dune nae wrang.
135 Dod and Davie slee-ly creep
in the hedgeback for a sleep.
Mucke feast o hens is gane,
nocht is left but yae hen-bane.
Tellin o that tale is dune –
140 third yin follies richt ahin.

Therr an then she lufts a ladle,
130 chases Gyppie roon the table.
Even though he's no tae blame,
he cries "Mercy!" aw the same.
Matt an Malkie, bit, they thiefs,
lie ootside ablow the leafs;
135 wan leg each, as ye kin see,
that's whit's left i thur chicken tea!
Therr's the seckint bag a tricks –
Terr the Thurd, it is, comes nixt.

An the muckle ladle – whack! –
lanns upo the doggie's back.
Ah, the pyne! He yowls lik gyte.
Fine he kens it's nae his wyte!
135 Far's the loons? Ey're nae tae finn –
hidlins, hoven, snocherin.
Far's the faest o rossen hens?
Naethin left but twaa shanks' enns!
Pliskie Nummer Twaa wes yon –
140 tae the neist we'se noo meeve on.

Fae da spön in weedow's haand
baffs an dunts on hund noo laand.
Wae he oobs an weel he micht
fir he kens he's dön bit richt.
135 Jarm an Jeemsie stentit foo
snores laek grice ahint a skroo.
Aa dat's left owre o dis footh
is a hen leg i der mooth.
Plunkie twa is here abön –
140 bit da tird een follows shön.

DRITTER STREICH

Jedermann im Dorfe kannte
Einen, der sich Böck benannte. –

  – Alltagsröcke, Sonntagsröcke,
  Lange Hosen, spitze Fräcke,
145 Westen mit bequemen Taschen,
  Warme Mäntel und Gamaschen –
  Alle diese Kleidungssachen
  Wußte Schneider Böck zu machen. –
  – Oder wäre was zu flicken,
150 Abzuschneiden, anzustücken,
  Oder gar ein Knopf der Hose
  Abgerissen oder lose –
  Wie und wo und was es sei,
  Hinten, vorne, einerlei –

EPISODE THREE

Everybody in the town,
knew of Mr. Buck's renown.

Working-clothes and Sunday best,
trousers, tailcoats, jacket, vest,
145 overcoats all fully lined,
garments of 'most any kind;
garter, gaiter, even spat –
Tailor Buck could make all that.
Or perhaps there was some mending,
150 lengthening, shortening or appending;
or a trouser-button loose,
thought to be of no more use –
how and where and whatsoever,
front and back, to patch or sever,

THORD SKEYLAAK

Aal the foak aboot the playis
kent the tyailor, Seppy Grayis.
Sep cud torn ees hand tiv owt –
naithin ivvor beat im – nowt!
145 Wark duds, weskits, Sunda bests,
gyaitors, ganzies, sharts an vests,
fancy breeks an britches bowld,
lang coats, short coats, caped an cowled,
baall goons, frocks an aprins braid,
150 petticoats an hats ee myade;
steetchin, hemmin, patchin, mends,
baiornies' bits frum odds an ends,
cuttins doon an stretchins oot,
easin, paddin, matchin cloots;

THORD THRICK

Near an far beyont the town
Tailor Buck had quare renown.
Sundy coats or workin clos,
tail coats pointin ti the toes,
145 britches, leggins, bum-freeze jackets,
waistcoats – all wi clivir pockets –
Tailor Buck cʌd fairly sew:
Damn the hate he didn't know!
Or if any clos wʌz wore,
150 buttons aff or throusers tore,
any work of any kine,
top or toe, firnenst, ahine,
darnin, stitchin, lettin out,
tikin in all sorts o clout,

THIRD PLOY

Goat the Teyler in the toun
was kent for miles and miles aroun.
Shiftin claes and Sabbath claes,
warm top-coats for wintry days,
145 lang-legg'd breeks and cutty cloaks,
weskits fou o handy pokes –
aa thir claes, or ocht bespak,
Teyler Goat richt weel could mak.
Skeelie, tae, to mend or patch,
150 cut them doon, add bits to match,
shew on buttons for your breeks,
had been tint or lowss for weeks;
hou or whar or what ye will
no a task owre ill to fill.

THURD TERR

Aw the folk fur miles aboot,
140 wantin troosers ur a suit,
wi weskit poackits rerr an haundy,
tails fur werrin oan a Sunday,
wurkin claes fur through the week,
jaikits, nicky-tams rale neat –
145 aw knew how tae come tae Boke,
Boke the Tailor aye could cope;
if claes need mendin, patcht ur sewn,
trooser buttons, say, pit oan,
frunt ur back, it disnae maitter,
150 Boke kin fix it, noo ur later,

THIRD PLISKIE

Ilkie bodie in the toon
kens aal Gait, the teylor loon.
Claes for Sabbath or the ouk,
warm quytes tae hap yer bouk,
145 queetikins an moggans lang,
weskits tee wi pooches strang,
tailie jaikets trig an braa,
Maister Gait cud mak em aa.
Hed ye ocht at needit sortin?
150 Ony duds tae cloot or shorten?
Hed ye e'er a button tint,
ruggit aff yer breeks ahint?
Foo or far or fit's tae dee,
fore or hint, fite'er it be,

PLUNKIE TREE

Lamb da tailor i dat place,
wis of coorse a weel kent face.
Wirkin plags an Sunday stroods,
ooen breeks an cotts wi hoods,
145 weskits at hed muckle pooches,
wirset froaks an aaldwives mutches,
siclaek claes athoot a scam
wis shön made bi mester Lamb.
If a jeckit wis owre stret
150 or a pair o breeks wis spret,
if a sark wis lost a button
or a torn skirt needit cuttin,
didna maitter whaar da sklent,
back or foreside, nivver ent –

155 Alles macht der Meister Böck,
Denn das ist sein Lebenszweck. –
–Drum so hat in der Gemeinde
Jedermann ihn gern zum Freunde. –
Aber Max und Moritz dachten,
160 Wie sie ihn verdrießlich machten.–

155 Buck did any alteration
for to sew was his vocation.
That is why around the county,
he had friends, and love and bounty.
Mac and Murray's greatest joy
160 was, however, to annoy.

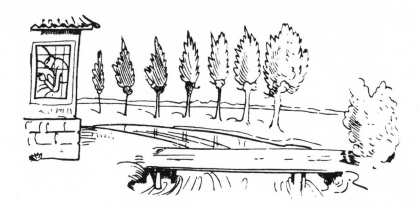

Nämlich vor des Meisters Hause
Floß ein Wasser mit Gebrause.
Übers Wasser führt ein Steg
Und darüber geht der Weg. –

Near Buck's house, so it would seem,
ran a rushing, gushing stream.
Crossing this there was a bridge,
with a foot-path on its ridge.

165 Max und Moritz, gar nicht träge,
Sägen heimlich mit der Säge,
Ritzeratze! Voller Tücke,
In die Brücke eine Lücke. –

165 Mac and Murray, never shirking,
got a saw and started working.
See-saw, see-saw, tap, tap, tap,
now the bridge has got a gap.

155 buttins, hyuks an een, as*tr*ay –
aal ti Seppy waas baiorns' play.
Foak aal kept on hees *r*eyght seyde;
nee yin huffs a fettlor's preyde!
'Cept fo twee aal huz kin nyame;
160 Meyk an Moas, the va*rr*y syame.
Oot-bi Seppy's doowor thor stud
Seppy's *br*ig o pyaintid wud,
lowpin owor the faior-seyzed born
ee'd ti c*r*oss hwior e'er he'd torn.
165 Hior, o corse, wor tyest*r*als twee
thowt ti wark sum woe an d*r*ee.
Wi a saa thi saad the planks
nigh on th*r*ewgh, faar f*r*um the banks.

155 Mr Buck no job wʌd shork –
tailorin wʌz his life's work.
That wʌz why the whole townlan
thought he wʌz a lekly man.
Mack an Maurice feelin bowl
160 planned ti bait this dacint sowl.
Right firnenst the tailor's dure
wʌz a shʌkh, yi can be sure.
Over this a wee bridge ran
lek a pad from lan ti lan.
165 Nir lame nir lazy, acting glick,
Mack an Maurice cut a nick.
With a saw they boxtied through,
nearly cut the planks in two!

155 Maister Goat tuik't aa the same,
pleasin folk was aye his aim.
Freind he was to ilka chiel,
freinds they were to him as weel.
But our callants had a ploy
160 Goat the Teyler to annoy.
By Goat's hous there was a water
rinnin fast wi noisy blatter.
Sen the burn was no that big,
plank o wuid serred as a brig.
165 Dod and Davie, hertless craturs,
thocht to brek the brig in smaithers,
skrechan-skrachan! wi the saw
nearly cut the brig in twa.

any joab, withoot a hitch –
that's his role in life, tae stitch.
Natcherally aw the folk
keep upsides wi Tailor Boke.
155 Matt an Malkie, bit, yon perr,
want tae see him terr his herr.
Anywey, ootside his door,
runs this burn wi a roar,
ablow a brig, made oot a plank,
160 keepin feet fae gettin damp.
Matt an Malkie, busy aye,
cut the widden brig hauf-wey,
saw it through, a sneaky trick,
rizzle-razz! tae weaken it.

155 Gait wad gledly sort yer claes –
yon's the darg o aa his days.
Sae, iss skeely, eident cheil
in the toon wes likit weel.
Mac an Matthy, tho – yon pair
160 thocht tae gar him rage an rair!
See, forenenst his fite door-steen
rins a burn wi cheerie creen.
Ere a buird wes pit tae lig
ower the watter for a brig.
165 Mac an Matthy tak a saa –
cut it hidlins near in twaa.
Bizzie-buzzie – sweirt ey're neen:
fegs, but fit a spite ey've deen!

155 wark laek dis ta Lamb dey broucht,
aa day lang wi leid he wroucht.
Sae it wis at aa da fock
laekit mester Lamb a lock.
Jarm an Jeemsie nane da less
160 nyaag will gie him an distress.
Bi da hoose whaar bed dis man,
white wi froad, a mill burn ran.
Owre da burn dey wir a brig,
hit led owre fae hoose ta rig.
165 Jarm an Jeemsie wirk awa
foo o filska wi da saa.
Skritty skratt, da tötaks strive,
i da plank a holl dey rive.

Als nun diese Tat vorbei,
170 Hört man plötzlich ein Geschrei:

Work complete, the wicked boys
170 start to shout and make a noise.

„He, heraus! du Ziegen-Böck!
Schneider, Schneider, meck meck meck!!" –
– Alles konnte Böck ertragen,
Ohne nur ein Wort zu sagen;
175 Aber wenn er dies erfuhr,
Ging's ihm wider die Natur. –

"Come on out, you boring Buck,
Tailor, Tailor, muck, muck, muck!"
Any trial or tribulation
Buck could bear with resignation;
175 but if anybody teased him
then a raging anger seized him.

Schnelle springt er mit der Elle
Über seines Hauses Schwelle,
Denn schon wieder ihm zum Schreck
180 Tönt ein lautes: „Meck, meck, meck!!"

Out he charges, wild and quick,
in his hand he holds a stick;
as the terrible refrain
180 "Muck, muck, muck", is heard again.

    Then thi hid ahint sum hwin,
170 settin up an aafu din:
    "Hwee's the daftist? Seppy Grayis!
    Seppy wi ees goniel fyace!
    Seppy dussint soe – ee howks!
    Seppy, ee's the preence o gowks!"
175 Sep waas meyld an eas'ly rooled,
    queyit, saft an kinda nooled,
    but yon fiorce camsteery storm
    i the end faior torned the wawm.
    Oot ee rusht on ti the brig –
180 Smash! It brok jist leyke a twig!

    When the saw wʌz all pʌt by
170 the pair o gets lets out a cry:
    "Hi there, Buckgoat, come an lʌk,
    tailor, tailor, muck, muck, muck!"
    Buck cʌd stan all sorts o fun,
    crack a joke wi anyone,
175 but this chik fair made him sore,
    he cʌd thole their lip no more.
    Mad wi rage, he tʌk his stick,
    out he run then brave an quick.
    Onct agane the culchees cried:
180 "Mucky Bucky, come outside!"

    Nou that darg is dune and by
170 suddent there is hard a cry!
    "Billy Goat, come out!" they geck,
    "Teyler, Teyler, meck, meck, meck!"
    Maister Goat could tak a lot,
    maistly he cared not a jot;
175 tholin thon frae onie cratur
    gaed agin his better natur.
    Pickin up his rule he tore
    smertly throu the open door.
    Yince agane the laddies geck
180 loudly at him, "Meck, meck, meck!"

165 Then the minit that joab's done,
    they shirrick Bokey, jist fur fun:
    "Tailor, come oan oot, weh-heh!
    stchupit goat-face, meh, meh, meh!"
    Boke could staun a loat a cheek,
170 shrug it aff withoot a peep,
    bit soon as thon perr stert tae laugh,
    Bokey jis aboot goes daft,
    grabs a yerdstick oot the hoose;
    at the door, comes merr abuse:
175 "Meh, meh, meh!" he hears the noise –
    shure enough, it's they bad boays.

    Fin the briggie's sinnert, swythe
170 comes a scraich, a lant sae blythe:
    "Teylor! Oot ye come, min! Heh!
    Billy-Gait, ye! Meh, meh, meh!"
    Maister Gait can thole it aa,
    ne'er a word he'll say ava.
175 Sic a jaa, tho, s' nae tae dree –
    noo he's in a tirravee!
    Up he lowps, his ellwann cleeks,
    swippert throu his aal door-cheeks,
    an he's seen rampadgin fair,
180 hearin "Meh, meh, meh!" eence mair!

    Whin der clooky wark wis owre,
170 dey begöd ta rout an roar:
    "Come doo oot, doo aalie lamb,
    tailor, tailor, yaarm, yaarm, yaarm."
    Skyimp or taant aald Lamb could dree,
    hit wis herd his löd ta jee.
175 Bit ta hear what dey him caa'd
    wis anyoch ta mak him mad.
    Wi a bismar in his nev,
    he da hoose in scad did lave.
    Fir eence mair ta mak him barm,
180 dis pair gölbröl "Yaarm, yaarm, yaarm."

Und schon ist er auf der Brücke,
Kracks! die Brücke bricht in Stücke;

There he is without ado –
Crack! The bridge has split in two,

Wieder tönt es: „Meck, meck, meck!"
Plumps! da ist der Schneider weg!

and with sounds of "muck, muck, muck",
gone from sight is Master Buck.

185 Grad als dieses vorgekommen,
Kommt ein Gänsepaar geschwommen,
Welches Böck in Todeshast
Krampfhaft bei den Beinen faßt.

185 Just as he is drowning fast,
so some geese come paddling past.
Buck grabs out, afraid of dying,
clutching tight as they start flying.

Dyun wint Seppy iv a flash,
roorin, raivin – hwaat a splash!
Poowor sowl, ee waas *trewly* glift
hwin ee foond eesel ad*r*ift;
185 till twee geese chanced dyun the spyate –
grabbin them, ee syailed i styate
ti the seyde an plodged ashoor;
steggored hyem an slammed ees doowor;

Wan good lep was all he p∧t –
the bridge jus give beneath his f∧t.
Onct agane they called out "Muck"
as headlong in went Mr Buck.
185 While the playboys t∧k aff fas
a pair o gees come swimmin pas.
At their legs, as quick as wink,
Buck grabs lek a dhrowndin tink;

Sune's he steps upon the brod –
crack! – brig flees aa owre the road.
"Meck, meck, meck!" agane they yatter.
Plop! the Teyler's in the water.
185 Juist as this stramash was boomin
doun the burn twa geese cam soomin.
Goat then, in the fear of Daith
gruppit fast a leg o baith.

Acroass the brig he belts, too true –
crack! the brig haufs right in two!
"Meh, meh, meh!" comes fae the bank –
180 splat! the tailor's doon the stank!
Therr goes Boke tae breathe his last,
an jis bi chance, two geese swum past;

On the brig his fit he pits –
Crack! the briggie braks tae bits!
"Meh, meh, meh!" soons oot bedeen –
Platch! an syne the teylor's geen!
185 Jist fin Gait hes teen his faa,
sweemin by come geesies twaa.
Gait, in reefu fear o daith,
clauchts the feeties o the baith.

Whin he sprits noo on da plank,
brokken hit anaeth him sank.
Lood dey roar oot: "Yaarm, yaarm, yaarm",
jöst afore he comes ta harm.
185 As he spricklin dere did lie,
twa fat geese cam soomin by.
Fir ta win oot fae da rip,
pipprin Lamb der legs did grip.

Beide Gänse in der Hand,
190 Flattert er auf trocknes Land. –

Goose and gander in each hand,
190 he succeeds in reaching land.

Übrigens bei alledem
Ist so etwas nicht bequem;

Incidentally, such events,
have their painful consequence.

Wie denn Böck von der Geschichte
Auch das Magendrücken kriegte.

Thus, to add to all his trouble,
Buck with cramp is bent up double.

soppin wet, bi sneezes *r*ent,
190 stummled tiv ees bed, weel spent …
Belly-wark st*r*uck i the neyght;
Mist*r*iss G*r*ayis hed thowt it meyght –
hoyed im on the p*r*essin-horse,
speyght ees heaves an hools an wawse;

wi a goose in eyer han
190 sprakhals out upon dhry lan.
Let me tell yi till yir face
acts lek this is out o place.
Poor owl Buck wʌz in a thromakh
wi the foundther in his stomach.

Baith the geese he had in hand
190 helped him flee upon dry land.
Onie road, forby, atweel,
’twas nae pleisand wey to feel;
aa thir ongauns were to blame
for sic grypin in his wame.

clamped aroon thum, lik grim death,
he gets a hudgie back tae earth.
185 It’s no much fun, that kinna trick,
it made puir Boke the tailor sick;
a kerry-oan, an nae mistake,
auld Boke’s suffrin fae gutsache.

Wi a geese in ilkie han,
190 see him flafferin tae the lan!
Saufit fae his ugsome plicht,
still ere somethin faar fae richt.
Aa iss steir hes gien peer Gait
in his wyme, a stoonin strait.

Wi a göse noo in each haand
190 flaachters he apo dry laand.
Yea, A’m shör doo will agree,
he wis fairly hed a spree,
caas wi aa dis cowld an damp
Lamb wis gotten sair bool cramp.

195 Hoch ist hier Frau Böck zu preisen!
    Denn ein heißes Bügeleisen

195 Here the highest praise is due
    to the Tailor's mistress, who

    auf den kalten Leib gebracht,
    Hat es wieder gut gemacht. –

    – Bald im Dorf hinauf, hinunter,
200 Hieß es: Böck ist wieder munter!!

    Dieses war der dritte Streich,
    Doch der vierte folgt sogleich.

    took the iron, cured the pain –
    made her husband well again.

    Thus it was that word got round,
200 Master Buck was safe and sound.

    That concludes the third bad deed –
    there are more, as you shall read.

195 plumped a het flat-*i*run *r*eyght
hweor it hort, form on ees keyte.
'Twaas hor sov*r*in *r*imiddy,
an it gaa*r*ed the colic flee.
Neor an faar, the fowuk went "Phew!" –
200 The fettlor waas as gud as new!
"Vic'*tr*y numbor th*r*ee", laaft Moas,
"noo wiv got thim bi the toas!"

195 Buck's brave missis wʌzn't slow,
knowed the things a wife shʌd know:
Tʌk the iron, made it hot
dh*r*ew out all the cowl he'd got.
Roun the town it soon was plain
200 Buck was at himself again.
That's the pakhals' thord bad th*r*ick –
the nix will folly in a tick.

195 Mistress Goat cam to his aid.
Sune a het flet-airn she laid
on's cauld kyte to ease the pain –
made him feel as richt as rain.
Round the toun the news has gane:
200 "Goat's alive and weel agane!"
Tellin o the third tale's dune –
fowrth yin follies richt ahin.

Here's his wife, bit, she's right able,
190 she brings oot the ironin-table,
runs the iron back an furrit
owre his gut – Boke soon recuvvert!
Wurd spread up an doon the toon,
"Boke's been cured!" the cry went roon.
195 Therr ye hud Terr Number Three –
noo here's Four, as ye kin see.

195 But his braa gweedwife sud get
aa the reese! An eyron het
saftly scaamin Gait's caal wyme,
sains the sair in little time.
Roon the crack gaes: "Eence again
200 Gait the teylor's hale an fain!"
Pliskie Nummer Three wes yön –
tae the neist we'se noo meeve on.

195 Gödwife Lamb here did her bit,
fir an iron at wis haet
shö sets noo apo his belly,
maks him better owre da helly.
Fock a Munanday noo hark:
200 "Lamb da day is back at wark".
Plunkie tree is here abön –
bit da fort een follows shön.

Vierter Streich

Also lautet ein Beschluß:
Daß der Mensch was lernen muß. –
205 – Nicht allein das A-B-C
Bringt den Menschen in die Höh;
Nicht allein im Schreiben, Lesen
Übt sich ein vernünftig Wesen;
Nicht allein in Rechnungssachen
210 Soll der Mensch sich Mühe machen;
Sondern auch der Weisheit Lehren
Muß man mit Vergnügen hören. –

Daß dies mit Verstand geschah,
War Herr Lehrer Lämpel da. –

Fourth Episode

As has frequently been stated
people must be educated.
205 Not alone the A, B, C,
heightens man's humanity;
not just simply reading, writing
makes a person more inviting;
nor does Arithmetic learning
210 make a pupil more discerning.
Reason, Wisdom, Moral Thought
must be equally well taught;

and to teach with erudition
was Professor Lample's mission.

Foworth Skeylaak

Larnt fowuk say, i heygh-flaan wards,
hyumun naychor speels tiwaads
205 noabilniss un noashins greyt,
eef in yuth wor set areyght,
bi wor pairints, preachors – ey,
an wor teachors, weyse an fley.
Plainor fowuk kens weel wi need
210 rules fo livvin fo ti heed,
bits a weesdim, provorbs, saas,
hyamely truths, reyght leevin's laas.
Maistor o the village skyul,
Biffy Laasun waas nee fyul;

Fourth Thrick

There's a sayin that diz go:
"Man mus larn while here below."
205 Tisn't jus the A, B, C
micks us what we have ti be;
tisn't larnin for ti write
micks a body torn out right;
tisn't jus be doin sums
210 that a body's long head comes:
But we hez ti hear wi pleasure
wise men teachin wisdom's threasure.
Of this sizim, wan example
ti us all was Masther Sample.

Fowrth Ploy

It was statute and decreed
whatna learnin Man wad need.
205 No alane the A B C
helps him heicher things comprie;
no alane can scrievin, readin,
gie the gumption that he's needin;
no alane wi sign and nummer
210 should a man his mind encummer
but tak pleisure in acquirin
Gift o Wisdom to inspire'm.
Wi sic thinkin aye to hand
Dominie Duncan took his stand.

Fourth Terr

Ah'm shure ye've oaften heard it statit,
people aw need edjicaitit;
no jis basic A B C,
200 readin, writin, wan, two, three;
if ye want tae get ahead,
it's wan thing bein widely read,
a whiz at coontin, very nice,
bit here's a piece a gude advice:
205 Wurds a wisdum's better stull,
people aye should drink thur full.
Teacher Lampwick in the skule
upheld right, bi rod an rule;

Fowert Pliskie

Ere a word at's aal an wyce:
Leir's a thing o muckle price.
205 Nae the A-B brod aleen
wullna mak ye snod an bein.
Kennin foo tae vreit an read
isna aa the mense ye need.
Coontin gies ye traachle sair,
210 but a slee cheil man ken mair.
Gweed aal-farrant smeddum –aye,
tent ye at, ye'll ken the wye!
Here, tae gar ye leir it weel,
Lintie, Maister o the Squeel!

Plunkie Fower

To' hit's true at ev'ry bairn
i dis wirld a lock man learn.
205 Learnin jöst da ABC
will dem little wisdom gie;
fock at can jöst write an read
hes in life a cuggly steid.
Ev'ry een at is alive
210 soodna jöst wi coontin strive,
bit sood hear tö, in bra löd,
aa da rules fir döin göd.
Teacher Tait wroucht wi his baand
sae dey wid dem understaand.

215 – Max und Moritz, diese beiden,
    Mochten ihn darum nicht leiden;
    Denn wer böse Streiche macht,
    Gibt nicht auf den Lehrer acht. –

    Nun war dieser brave Lehrer
220 Von dem Tobak ein Verehrer,
    Was man ohne alle Frage
    Nach des Tages Müh und Plage
    Einem guten alten Mann
    Auch von Herzen gönnen kann. –

225 – Max und Moritz, unverdrossen,
    Sinnen aber schon auf Possen,
    Ob vermittelst seiner Pfeifen
    Dieser Mann nicht anzugreifen. –

215 Mac and Murray, as a whim,
    took a strong dislike to him.
    Those intent on pranks, you see,
    do not heed Philosophy.

    Now – the Master took great pleasure,
220 in his well-earned hour of leisure,
    to relax into a coma
    with tobacco's lush aroma;
    which, to end a hard day's drudge,
    is a joy one can't begrudge.

225 Shameless Murray, reckless Mac,
    once again devised attack;
    and they thought the time was ripe,
    to play tricks with Lample's pipe.

215 kent fu weel wor baiorns need mair
than the three Rs — need it sair.
*R*eadin, *R*eytin, *R*ithmittic;
ey, but *R*eet an *R*ang's the trick.
He hissel had yin weak spot —
220 luvved ees peype an aafu lot;
speshly wi the day's wark dyun,
hwin the baiorns hed hyemwaad *r*un.
'Twaas nee *v*arry *g*reet uffence;
nyen wud sleyght ees sense or mense
225 jist fo feyndin plizhor *r*eype
in ees aad dad's meershum peype.
Wor twee donned thor theenkin caps,
picked the best o siv'*r*al traps ...

215 Mack an Maurice for this cause
hated Masther S. lek taws:
Wisdom always micks yi sick
if you're a boy that lecks a thrick.
This masther now had wan wee vice,
220 thought a clay was powerful nice.
Wan good smoke before his bed
surely helped ti shire his head,
for the pleasure of a cuddy
lifts the mine of anybody.
225 Mack an Maurice, bowl as brass
for this masther hez no mass;
think that it would be a joke
ti spoil an owl man's quiet smoke.

215 Dod and Davie, bad boys baith,
to agree wi him were laith;
they that wicked are indeed
to the Maister pey nae heed.
This fine teacher at the schuil
220 lo'ed his baccy-pipe richt weel;
days o darg wi moil and fricht
deserve a pipe to soothe at nicht;
hertless he that wad deny
guid auld man his pipe forby!
225 Dod and Dave, wi muckle joy
had in mind to play a ploy —
Dominie Duncan's hous to rype
seekin there the Maister's pipe.

Matt an Malkie, ay, yon perr,
210 shut thur ears, jis didnae kerr;
them thit's ayewis giein cheek,
nivver hears the teacher speak.
Lampwick wis a decent bloke,
above aw else he liked his smoke,
215 tae full his pipe up wi tabacca;
efter wurk, ye cannae whack a
pipe a peace, tae sook at leisure —
who'd deny the sowl his pleasure?
Matt an Malkie, ay, ye've guessed,
220 singulurly unimpressed,
rack thur brains fur wan merr joke —
mibbe get him through his smoke?

215 Mac an Matthy, nickums twaa,
cudna thole the man ava.
Fin ere pliskies ull tae dee,
fa wad heed the dominie?
Noo, iss braa chiel hed ae lack: a
220 mangin for the reek o bacca.
Ne'er ye'll threep at sic a mannie,
wyce an eident, aal an canny,
efter aa the darg o's day,
iss smaa pleisur sudna hae!
225 Mac an Matthy wurna slaa
thinkin foo tae play a chaa,
plottin weys tae gowk an gype
Maister Lintie — wi his pipe!

215 Jarm an Jeemsie, I man tell,
aaber wis dis sheeld ta fell.
Bairns at hatter fock an rant
teachers' wirds will nivver ant.
Noo dis man o chaalk an books
220 eence a day some bacha rooks.
Whin his wark in schöl he whets,
fae da skelf his pipe he gets.
Wha o wis wid ever say
nae aald man sic joy sood hae?
225 Jarm an Jeemsie, owresteer boys,
still ir wirkin oot new ploys.
Shön wan tocht der heads dös fill:
Öse his pipe ta dö him ill!

– Einstens, als es Sonntag wieder
230 Und Herr Lämpel, brav und bieder,

One fine Sunday, we are told,
230 as good Lample, honest, bold,

In der Kirche mit Gefühle
Saß vor seinem Orgelspiele,
Schlichen sich die bösen Buben
In sein Haus und seine Stuben,
235 Wo die Meerschaumpfeife stand;
Max hält sie in seiner Hand;

went to church and with emotion
played the organ for devotion –
so the naughty boys with guile,
crept into the house meanwhile
235 where the pipe was wont to stand.
Mac here holds it in his hand.

Aber Moritz aus der Tasche
Zieht die Flintenpulverflasche,
Und geschwinde, stopf, stopf, stopf!
240 Pulver in den Pfeifenkopf. –

Murray is the wicked one
who finds powder from a gun.
This into the pipe they stuff
240 till the bowl is full enough.

Sunda cummed, hwin Biffy'd plyay
230 at the orgin, cum hwaat may,
as ee did each Sunda neyght,
jiggin feet an haunds i fleyght.
Oot wint he an in wint they –
Cat awaa, the meyce wud plyay.
235 Syun thi foond ees peype, ees dior,
wheor ee kept it, bey ees chior;
packt the grand, lang-seasind bool
wi gunpoodor nigh on fooll;
then a baccy theak on top,
240 fo ti ketch im on the hop;

Sundy mornin come again
230 Masther Sample right as rain
tʌk his sate firnenst the choir
played ti God wi sowl on fire.
These two playboys, deft as doom
tiptoed in wir good man's room
235 where his lovely pipe was set.
Mack soon picked it up, the get;
while young Maurice, fʌll o scorn
tʌk gun powdher from a horn,
hil' it still, an by my sowl
240 poured the lot intil the bowl.

Sunday was the best time, than;
230 Dominie Duncan, honest man,
gaed intil the kirk to play
at the organ on that day.
Thae bad laddies smooled intil
Duncan's hous sae quate and still;
235 when the meerschaum pipe they fand
Dodie held it in his hand;
Davie frae his pooch has won
flask o pouther for a gun,
stapped the pouther in the bowl
240 o the Maister's pipe, puir sowl!

Anyhow, oan Sunday moarnin,
while auld Lampwick played the oargan
225 in the church, wi bags a style –
this auld fulla, gaun his mile –
yon perr snuck inside his hoose,
an fun his study, wherr he used
tae keep his pipe, his faivrit smoke;
230 Matt uplifts it, here's the joke –
Malkie tims gunpowder in,
a hale flask full, a wickit sin –
pokes it doon the bowl, the scamp,
lik best tabacca, tamp, tamp, tamp!

Eence fin on a Sabbath day,
230 leal an stainch, he'd geen tae play
meesic braa as ye cud list
on the Kirk's aal fussle-kist,
ben his hoose an room ey smool,
yon twaa geeties bringin dool,
235 far his fine braa pipe ay staans:
Ere's it noo in wee Mac's hans.
Fae the pooch in Matthy's breeks
oot a pooder-flask he cleeks.
Puff-puff-puff – richt gleg ey wap it –
240 noo the bowle's wi pooder stappit!

Whin it wis da Sabbath day
230 an aald Tait in kirk did play,
as he sat fair prood an prunk,
didna he da organ runk!
Dan da reebalds hint inby,
trow his hoose dey mak der wye,
235 win ta whaar da great pipe staands;
Jarm noo taks hit in his haands.
Jeemsie dan oot o his pooch
wi a laach gunpooder fötch.
Yea, dis boy he is nae sloo,
240 fills da pipe near stappit foo.

Jetzt nur still und schnell nach Haus,
Denn schon ist die Kirche aus. –

– Eben schließt in sanfter Ruh
Lämpel seine Kirche zu;

Quietly, quickly, off they go –
church is over – none must know! –

Master Lample here you see
locks the church and turns the key.

245 Und mit Buch und Notenheften,
Nach besorgten Amtsgeschäften
Lenkt er freudig seine Schritte
Zu der heimatlichen Hütte,

245 With tranquillity and calm,
books and music 'neath his arm,
he enjoys work's aftermath
as he takes the homeward path;

Und voll Dankbarkeit sodann
250 Zündet er sein Pfeifchen an.

and content in attitude
250 lights his pipe with gratitude.

put it back wi luvvin cior
whior thi'd foond it, bi ees chior ...
Doon the street the sarvis ends;
aal the gud fowuk hyemwaad wends.
245 Hyem cums Biffy, dooty diun,
bleezes up ees feyor siun,
hoys ees myussic on a seat,
sets ees coffee-pot ti heat,
leefts ees peype up tiv ees gob,
250 finnds it fu, sez: "Jist the job!",

Come now quick! Don't hang about!
Folks from chorch is comin out.
Ano'er meetin passed wi aise
ticks his music an his kays,
245 Sample shuts the chorch dure tight
goin home an feelin right.
On he goes wi ket-light gait
longin for his earthly thrait.
Down he sits ti leisure sweet
250 lights the pipe, pʌts up the feet.

Quick and quate for hame they hail
as the kirk begoud to skail.
Duncan, in guid tid, and free,
locked the kirk door wi his key,
245 oxtered music sheets and Buik,
wi a proud official look
linkit at it canty, crouse
to his ain wee cosy hous.
Feelin fou o gratitude
250 to licht his pipe he syne begoud.

235 Aff hame then the bad boays scoot,
jist as church sterts comin oot.
Lampwick noo, his mind at ease,
loacks the door, an takes his keys,
his hymn-buke an his music-sheet,
240 an duty done, turns up the street
towards his hoose, his hert's abode,
trippin gaily up the road.
Wance inside, he lights his pipe,
an settles doon, contented-like.

Hame ey're snoovin – quick, A trou,
for the Kirk's tae skail eenou.
Weel content, the dominie
steeks the door an turns the key.
245 Noo he's deen his canny stent,
taks his meesic-buiks wi tent,
syne he's aff, sae blythe an douce,
til his canty wee bit hoose.
Fou o thanks, he gies a rype
250 til his stove, an lunts his pipe.

Laek twa mice noo hame dey smoot,
fir da kirk will shön be oot.
Tait in göd lay here we see
as da kirkdoor he dös key.
245 Feenished noo is sermon time,
sae wi book o psalm an hyme
foo o blydeness he dös stend
up da gaet ta his but-end.
An wi tankfoo hert dat nicht
250 tae his pipe he hadds a licht.

„Ach!" – spricht er – „die größte Freud
Ist doch die Zufriedenheit!!!"

"Ah", he says, "a man's best friend
is contentment, in the end."

Rums!! – da geht die Pfeife los
Mit Getöse, schrecklich groß.
255 Kaffeetopf und Wasserglas,
Tobaksdose, Tintenfaß,
Ofen, Tisch und Sorgensitz –
Alles fliegt im Pulverblitz. –

Bang, crash, bang! The pipe's explosion
causes havoc and erosion.
255 Stove and table, chair and couch,
ink-pot and tobacco-pouch,
glass and cup and coffee-pot,
bang goes Master Lample's lot!

tyeks the tongs an nips a cooul,
sets it, bornin, ti the booul,
hes a forst an welcum, *d*raa,
feels contintmint waamly *g*raa,
255 seyghs an *reachiz for* ees – BOOUM!
Blast an *b*reyght flash fill the *r*ooum!
Back ee flees an cowps ees *c*reels,
sees the ceilin past ees heels,

"Ah," says he, "the whole worl roun
nothin's leck contentmen foun."
Bang, wham, boom, bedang and fizz!
Busted pipe! A powerful bizz!
255 Coffee-pot an crooshkeen lawn,
snuff-box, tumler an ink-stan,
table, stove, his good saf chair
all go whirtlin through the air!

"Ah!" quo he, "Man's greatest pleasure
is contentment in his leisure!"
WOOF! The meerschaum pipe explodes,
fearsome BANG sends gear aa roads.
255 Water-joug and coffee-pat
sneeshin-mill, inkhorn I wat,
stove and table, easy chair
wi the blast flee ilkawhar.

245 "Ay," says he, "Repose is best.
There's nothing like a well-earned rest."
KABOOM! Jist then his pipe blew up!
Inkwell, coaffee-poat an cup,
table, stove, his gude tabacca,
250 ivrythin, a jug a watter,
whoosh! went flyin through the err –
Lampwick in his easy cherr!

"Aye", says he, "Nae greater pleasure
nor contentment in such measure!"
FLIST! The pipe's tae smiddrins dung,
wi a belter o a bung!
255 Inkwaal an tobacca-box,
gless an trackie, aa the crocks,
cheir, stove, table, flee aa throu'der
wi the fuffin o the pooder!

"Ya", he says, "der naethin better
As a hame 'thoot nyarg an nyitter".
Bang! His pipe is laid in coom
wi a maist oondömious boom.
255 Aa da lem an siclaek gear,
oven, table, restin shair,
bacha-box an aald taecup,
trow da air gings fleein up.

Als der Dampf sich nun erhob,
260 Sieht man Lämpel, der gottlob!
Lebend auf dem Rücken liegt;
Doch er hat was abgekriegt.

As the smoke begins to clear,
260 Lample is seen lying here,
still alive, thank God, but wait –
not quite in his usual state.

Nase, Hand, Gesicht und Ohren
Sind so schwarz als wie die Mohren,
265 Und des Haares letzter Schopf
Ist verbrannt bis auf den Kopf. –

Black are face and nose and lips,
black right to his finger-tips.
265 And his last few strands of hair,
burnt to cinders – none are there!

feynds eesel flat on ees back,
260   iv a *rooum* syut-filled an black ...
Theor's ees coffee-pot – in bits!
Bacca-tin aal b*r*ays an splits!
Peype i bittocks, warst uv aal –
baar the mee*r*or on the waall!
265   Hwees yon black fyace i the glass?
Is't Aad Neeck, then, bowld as b*r*ass?
Na! 'Tsimsel, baald as a peor –
gyen ees haior an eeb*r*oos faior!

When the smoke an stoor all clears
260   Sample on his back appears.
Thanks ti God, wir man's not dead
but he hez a wile sore head!
Chullers, hans, eyes, ears an nose,
black as Toal's coat wʌz his clos,
265   gone his wan las rib o hair,
borned his brow an black an bare.

When the reek had blawn awa
260   God be praised, our man we saw
live, but lyin there wi scaurs
like he had been in the wars.
Neb and hands and lugs and face
wad a bleckamoor disgrace;
265   ilka hair that ever grew
on his powe is brunt enoo.

Wance the stoor cleared, though, thanks be,
therr wis Lampwick, as ye see,
255   stretcht oot flat, an breathin yit.
Stull, he's suffert quite a bit –
hauns, an eyes, an ears an nose,
burnt as black as auld black Joe's;
his precious heid a herr distroyed –
260   a bauldy-bane, wis he annoyed!

See, fin aa the reek's awaa,
260   Lintie's corp? Be thankit, na!
Flatlins on the fleer ligs he,
live, but wi a haep tae dree!
Neb an lugs an hans an face
lik a Blaik o Moorish race.
265   An his scaap is scowdert bare
o the last wee flaacht o hair!

Whin da reek noo dwines awa,
260   we see Tait's no dead ava,
bit jöst lyin in a dwaam.
You'll agree he's no da sam,
fir his haand, his face, his broo,
wis noo mirk as shaela oo.
265   Collcoomed wis his tiv o hair,
hit, ill trift, will growe nae mair.

Wer soll nun die Kinder lehren
Und die Wissenschaft vermehren?
Wer soll nun für Lämpel leiten
270 Seine Amtestätigkeiten?
Woraus soll der Lehrer rauchen,
Wenn die Pfeife nicht zu brauchen??

Mit der Zeit wird alles heil,
Nur die Pfeife hat ihr Teil. –

275 Dieses war der vierte Streich,
Doch der fünfte folgt sogleich.

Who will now bring Youth their learning?
Feed their scientific yearning?
Who will now fill Lample's station
270 in the church administration?
How will Lample smoke again
now his pipe is broke in twain?

Wounds and ills will heal in time,
but the pipe succumbed to crime.

275 That concludes the fourth bad deed –
there are more, as you shall read.

Hwaat on orth waas ee ti dee?
270 Thees the baiorns must nivvor see –
Ee'd nat gan ti kirk or skyul
lukkin leyke a wawkin skull.
Sa ee hid eesel frum seyght,
beydin till ees haior waas reyght –
275 Teyme ti wark oot hwey an hoo
'twaas ees weel-treyd bacca blew!
"Foworth vic'try!" sniggord Meyke,
"teyme to win the fift un, leyke!"

Who's now goin ti larn the weeans,
show them how till use their brains?
Poor owl Sample's in the lorch –
270 Who'll tick meetins in the chorch?
What can this good crather smoke
now his bes pipe is all broke?
Aw'er bardicks can be mended,
but the Meerschaum's days is ended.
275 That's the buckos' fourth bad torn –
read the res, now don't adjorn.

Wha will learn the scholars nou,
spreidin wittan leal and true?
Wha is stieve eneuch to tak
270 official duties on his back?
What will Dominie Duncan smoke
nou his meerschaum pipe is broke?
Time heals aa, as is weel kend.
No the pipe! It winna mend!
275 Tellin o the fowrth tale's dune –
fift yin follies richt ahin.

Noo who's gonny teach the weans,
full thur heid wi facks an names?
Who'll take oan auld Lampwick's task,
an dae his wurk? Ye might well ask.
265 An whit's the teacher gonny smoke,
noo his faivrit pipe's goat broke?
Time heals aw, ur so it should,
bit no the pipe, hit's done fur gude.
That's the Fourth Terr noo jis by –
270 Five comes nixt, an that's nae lie.

Fa's tae leir the littleens noo,
souch o wyceheid in his mour?
Fa's tae staan in Lintie's steid,
270 teachin bairns tae vreit an read?
Fit gin for a smeek he's wishin,
noo his pipe's tae crockanition?
Time haels aa things, late or seen,
but the aal pipe's day is deen.
275 Pliskie Nummer Fower wes yon –
tae the neist we'se noo meeve on.

Wha sall noo da schölbairns teach
an da rules o booklear preach?
Wha sall noo wi blackboard varg
270 an at döless young eens sharg?
Foo sall Tait his pipe noo rook?
Hit lies brokken in a nyook.
Time alane maks aathing hale,
bit da pipe's anidder tale.
275 Plunkie fowr is here abön –
bit da fift een follows shön.

FÜNFTER STREICH

Wer in Dorfe oder Stadt
Einen Onkel wohnen hat,
Der sei höflich und bescheiden,
280 Denn das mag der Onkel leiden. –
– Morgens sagt man: „Guten Morgen!
Haben Sie was zu besorgen?"
Bringt ihm, was er haben muß:
Zeitung, Pfeife, Fidibus. –
285 Oder sollt es wo im Rücken,
Drücken, beißen oder zwicken,
Gleich ist man mit Freudigkeit
Dienstbeflissen und bereit. –

EPISODE FIVE

Uncles, wheresoe'er they are,
living near, or living far,
like politeness and respect –
280 uncles do not like neglect.
In the morning one must say,
"'Morning, how are you today?"
One must carry, run and fetch,
bring him paper, pipe and 'Sketch';
285 or again should he complain
of a back-ache, twinge or pain,
one must be alert and heed
to his every wish and need;

FIFT SKEYLAAK

Toon an village, ivriwhior,
280 foak ey gi thor unkils caior.
Canny an poleyte thor steyle,
riddy wi the morn-breyght smeyle:
"Hwaat's yor fettle, then, the day?
Yor lukkin canny, ony way!"
285 Offorin thor helpin hans;
fetchin pyaipors, peypes, ale-cans;
dreyvin aff the waasps an flees,
hwen ee snoozes nigh the trees;
runnin fo the lineemint
290 eef ee's hippint up ahint.

FITH THRICK

If yir uncle's near yir place
let yir works be fʌl o grace.
Allus thry ti thrait him dacint;
280 he will fine that quare'n playsant.
Every dawn say: "Mornin, hey!
Any messages the day?"
Get whativer he wʌd leck:
paper, pipe or match ti streck;
285 or if somethin leck a midge
bites his back or micks him fidge,
You shʌd allus be right glad
ti pandher till his every fad.

FIFT PLOY

Wha in toun or kintraside
has an uncle wi him bide,
should be mensefu and polite –
280 in that his uncle will delyte.
"Mornin til ee" dae ye say,
"is there ocht ye want the day?"
Bring him aa he needs: the paper,
pipe and spunks, aiblins a taper.
285 Gif something at his back is grippin
pokin, prickin, kittlin, nippin,
are ye gled to be at hand
meetin ilka smaa demand?

FIFTH TERR

Disnae maitter wherr ye stey,
respeck yir uncle, that's the wey.
Toon ur country, be polite,
that's whit uncles maistly like.
275 "Moarnin, Uncle!" 's whit ye say,
"Anythin ye want the day?"
Bring him anythin he'd like,
paper, matches, ur his pipe;
if thurs sumthin giein hin gyp,
280 pain, say, in his back ur hip,
you'll be therr, withoot a doot,
helpin puir auld Uncle oot.

FIFT PLISKIE

Fa in clachan or in toon
hes an uncle bidin roon,
man be douce an fou o mense
280 sae's tae dee him nae offence.
Ilkie mornin, "Fair gweed day!
Can A sair ye?" ye sud say.
Syne ye fess fite'er he wunts:
journal, bacca-pipe, or lunts.
285 Gin a stoonin thraa or rack
pynes yer uncle in his back,
gleg ye'll rin tae gie a han,
sain the stang as best ye can.

PLUNKIE FIVE

Maist young fock an uncle hae
bidin i dis isles an sae;
dey sood moad'rate be an göd
280 fir ta pit him in braa löd.
Whin dey meet him dey sood say:
"Foo can I help you da day?"
Dan dey bring him whaat he's waantin,
paper, bacha, pipe or pantin.
285 If his craig or rig is yucky,
he sood tink he is da lucky,
'caas his oy dat very oor
is richt dere an will him cloor;

Oder sei's nach einer Prise,
290 Daß der Onkel heftig niese,
Ruft man „Prosit!" allsogleich,
„Danke, wohl bekomm es Euch!" –
Oder kommt er spät nach Haus,
Zieht man ihm die Stiefel aus,
295 Holt Pantoffel, Schlafrock, Mütze,
Daß er nicht im Kalten sitze –
Kurz, man ist darauf bedacht,
Was dem Onkel Freude macht. –
– Max und Moritz ihrerseits
300 Fanden darin keinen Reiz. –
Denkt euch nur, welch schlechten Witz
Machten sie mit Onkel Fritz! –

or if snuff is what he pleases,
290 which results in hefty sneezes,
one must not forget to call
"Bless you". – "Thank you". – "Not at all!"
Or if Uncle comes home late,
boots off quick, he must not wait;
295 fetch his slippers, cap and gown,
never let an Uncle down!
Thus a duty one must treasure
is to give one's Uncle pleasure.
Mac and Murray, though, we find
300 saw no point in being kind.
Hear what trick they played instead
on their poor old Uncle Fred! –

Let im cum in eftor daak,
an thor's bussle, fuss an squaak;
ivribody rushin up,
slippors fetcht, an styeamin cup,
295 dressin goon an flannen cap.
Let im sneeze jist yince an – snap! –
sic i bedlim: "Tck-tck-tcks",
"Bless yis", "Fetch the rums", "Waam breecks"!
Yon's the way foaks aare, yi see,
300 wi unkils whee aare weel-ti-dee.
Meyk an Moas, but, pyaid nee heed
tiv ivribody else's creed:
Steed, thi sleyly wawked oot hoo
thi'd git Unkil iv i stew,

If he ticks a pinch o snuff
290 sneezes wi a mighty huff,
you shʌd say when he hez thundhered:
"May yi live ti be a hundherd!"
Or if he comes home quite late,
pʌll the boots from aff his fate,
295 get his slippers an his snood,
his dhressin-gown ti warm him good.
Thrait him well, do all yi can –
mick o him the happy man.
Mack an Maurice for their part
300 didn't show they had a heart.
Jus lʌk how they played a prank,
tʌk the smile aff Uncle Frank.

Gif he gies an unco sneeze
290 efter's sneeshin, does it please
t' say "God bliss ye!" and "Guid helt!
Fegs but ye are welcome til't!"
Hameward late at nicht he cam –
did ye pour him out a dram,
295 fetch his slippers, cap, and goun,
bield frae cauld when he sat doun?
Thocht ye than o ilka plan
wad mak the chiel a happy man?
Dod and Davie, for their pairt
300 fand nae merit in that airt.
Think ye on the ill-faured joke
they yince played on Uncle Jock.

If he takes a pinch a snuff,
an sneezes too hard, shure enough,
285 you're instanter tae the rescue,
shout "Gesundheit, Uncle! Bless you!"
If he gets hame late an tired,
take his buits aff bi the fire,
fetch his baffies, goon an hat,
290 so's he'll no be cauld 'n that.
In shoart, ye'll dae whit aw ye can,
tae make his life a happy wan.
Matt an Malkie, bit, aw naw,
didnae kerr fur this at aw.
295 Watch them rack thur wickit brains
tae play a trick oan Uncle James!

Gin the nip o sneesh he prees
290 gars him gie a muckle neeze,
"Seel befaa ye!" ye man cry,
"Aa gweed hale an machts for ay!"
Gin he's late, fae mony trachles,
pou his beets aff, get his bachles,
295 hoose-quyte, hoomet – sae's the aal
mannie wullna stairve wi caal.
An in soom, ye'll ay be redd
aakyn weys tae mak him gled.
Sic gweed deeins, weel A'se warran,
300 Mac an Matthy fann nae bar in.
Jist jalouse the nesty bam
yon twaa played on Uncle Tam!

or whin staandin in a breeze,
290 dis aald man begins ta neeze,
oy cries oot ta uncle: "Bliss you."
Uncle says: "I tank dee – Haa choo!"
If he comes hame late at nicht,
oy will rivlins lowse at's ticht,
295 pit a kyep on head at's baald,
sae he dösna catch da caald.
Oy is aft at uncle's side,
jöst ta mak da aald sheeld blyde.
Jarm an Jeemsie, fir der pairt,
300 toucht dis wis a lock o dirt.
Shön we'll see whaat kind o foally
dey hed dem wi uncle Olly.

Jeder weiß, was so ein Mai-
Käfer für ein Vogel sei. –

Everybody knows the May-
bug that flies around all day.

305   In den Bäumen hin und her
        Fliegt und kriecht und krabbelt er.

305   In the trees it flits about,
        creeping, crawling in and out.

Max und Moritz, immer munter,
Schütteln sie vom Baum herunter.

Mac and Murray, full of glee,
shake the may-bugs off the tree.

In die Tüte von Papiere
310   Sperren sie die Krabbeltiere. –

Then the crawly beasts are stacked
310   and in paper-bags are packed,

305 wi cockcheffors, haard as nyails,
tweetchy-bells wi claain tyails,
*g*reet black clocks that, maior an maior,
thi collectid iv*r*iwhior,
shyaikin them *f*rum sh*r*ub an *t*ree,
310 fillin pyaipor bags wi glee.
Wi this host o captif bugs,
thi'd ha Unkil bi the lugs –

Everybody knows the clocks
that crawl in threes an breed in crocks.
305 Near ti wʌdz they can be foun
flyin, creepin, wigglin roun.
On the sly, wir Mick an Maurice
shake the dewels from the fores',
then colleck the nippin yokes
310 ketchin them in paper pokes.

We aa ken, baith ye and hiz,
whatna beast the bum-cloke is,
305 'mang the trees, abuin, about,
fleein, crawlin, keekin out.
Dod and Davie, fou o glee,
shog the clokers aff the tree.
In paper pokes, to hasten maitters
310 stuff the creepie-crawlie craturs.

Ye'll know, cuz ivrybuddy diz,
whit kinna burd a bumcloack is.
Fleein in an oota trees
300 ye get thum, crawlin owre the leaves.
Matt an Malkie, nivver done,
shake doon beetles tae the grun,
an gether up in paper pokes
aw thon creepy-crawly cloacks.

Seerly ilkie een o hiz
kens fit beast a goloch is.
305 Up the trees ey're aa aboot,
creepin, fleein in an oot.
Mac an Matthy, chaav'n awa,
shak the tree, an doon ey faa.
Intil twistit paper pyockies
310 syne ey stap the crowlin bockies.

Der nae doot maist croftin fock
kens a boag caa'd hundiclock.
305 I da voar or simmer he
aft will oag apo a tree.
Jarm an Jeemsie, filsket twa,
shiggles herd an maks dem faa.
In twa pockies noo is pitten
310 ev'ry oagin clock dey mitten.

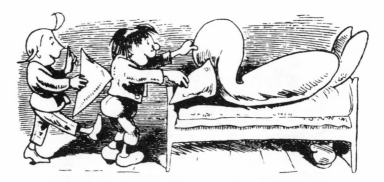

Fort damit, und in die Ecke
Unter Onkel Fritzens Decke!

taken – with no trace of guilt –
hidden under Uncle's quilt.

Bald zu Bett geht Onkel Fritze
In der spitzen Zippelmütze;
315 Seine Augen macht er zu,
Hüllt sich ein und schläft in Ruh.

Here you see good Uncle Fred
just about to go to bed;
315 lying down – his eyes are closing
and already he is dosing.

'caas thi hid them iv ees tick
till the poowor man's bed waas hwick!
315　Unkil gans ti bed yon neyght,
gooned an capped an bed-socked *r*eyght;
tucks hissel in gyainst the caad,
shuts ees een, *r*ilaxin, glaad ...

Then the clocks is quickly pʌt
in Frank's bed, jus by the fʌt.
Wi his pointy nightcap on
Uncle Frank begins ti yawn,
315　tucks the eidherdown in tight,
shuts the eyes ti sleep the night.

When the pokes are nearly fillt
pit them under Uncle's quilt.
Uncle Jock gangs up to bed
in cutty sark and nicht-cap cled,
315　steeks his een and coories in,
restfu sleep comes to him sune.

305　Nixt they tim thur pokes well-fillt,
under Uncle Jimmy's quilt!
James goes up tae bed hauf-deid,
pixie nightcap owre his heid,
settles doon, gets well rowed up,
310　soon draps, aff, his eyes tight shut.

See noo far the breets ey're pittin –
in aneth aal Tammie's queetin!
Seen Tam thinks in's bed tae coorie,
in his hoomet wi the toorie.
315　Steeks his een an cuddles doon–
in a tick he's sleepin soon.

Dan fir Olly's hoose dey med,
hoidet dem athin his bed.
Shön comes uncle Olly wearin
nichtplags an a candle bearin,
315　wi a soch he steeks his een,
snores anaeth da coonterpeen.

Doch die Käfer, kritze, kratze!
Kommen schnell aus der Matratze.

But the may-bugs – scritch, scratch, scrawl –
now begin their upward crawl.

    Schon faßt einer, der voran,
320 Onkel Fritzens Nase an.

    Look! The one who is ahead,
320 bites the nose of Uncle Fred.

„Bau!!" – schreit er – „was ist das hier?!!"
Und erfaßt das Ungetier.

"Wow!" he yells, "what have we here?"
reaching for the bug that's near.

Screech-scrach! Screech-scrach-screech-scrach-screech!
320 *Russle-scruffle-scriffle-screech!*
Ee! Hwaat's teeckling at ees toas?
Wow! Hwaativvor's nipped ees noas?
Hweese the thoosind maarchin feet
stampin owor im i the heat?

Up the quilt wi 'ticks' an 'tocks'
comes a line o marchin clocks,
an their leadher bravely goes
320 up till Uncle Franky's nose.
"Heugh!" he scrakes an in his shock
micks a grab an gets the clock.

Syne the clokers in a press
blouter out o the matress.
The first and foremaist in the race
320 grups the neb on Uncle's face.
"Cripes!" he screiched, "What hae we here?"
and flang the nesty beastie clear.

While auld Jimmy's fast asleep –
scribble, scrabble, oot they creep!
Up the quilt the leader goes,
the heid bumcloack, an nips his nose.
315 "Ohh!" shouts James, "whit's this we've goat?!!"
an grabs the bumcloack bi the throat.

But or lang, wi unco scartin,
fae the claes the clocks come startin!
Fit a cheek the foremaist hes –
320 nippin Uncle Tammie's nizz!
"Hech! Fit's iss!" gowls Tam in fear,
snickin aff the ugsome skeer.

Bit da clocks come, skarty-skrit,
owre da bedclaes yasp dey sprit.
Tae da tap da first een rips,
320 Uncle Olly's neb hit grips.
"Gaadge, whaat's dis?" he bröls in shock,
as he yocks da ill-laek clock.

Und den Onkel voller Grausen,
Sieht man aus dem Bette sausen.

In disgust and in dismay,
he attempts to run away.

325 „Autsch!!" – Schon wieder hat er einen
Im Genicke, an den Beinen;

Hin und her und rund herum
Kriecht es, fliegt es mit Gebrumm.

325 Ouch! another takes a peck
in the legs and in the neck.

Up and down and everywhere
may-bugs fill the floor and air.

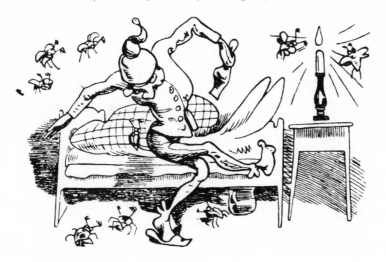

325 Unkil, but, 's o stordy breed –
    oot o bed ee's shaapish fleed,
    draggin aal the beddin doon,
    starmin, stampin, slappin, roon.
    Lowpin ivrihwior waas ee,
330 hoyin eensecks heck an jee –

    Scarred ti death he ups an out
    flingin dishabels about.
325 Hekh! a dewel's on his nack,
    at his legs he gives a whack,
    crawlin, flyin to an fro,
    up an down the buggers go.

    Uncle Jock, wi horror struck,
    lowpit out o bed gey quick.
325 "Outsh!" At that he taks a straik
    at yin that's crawlin doun his neck.
    Here and there and gaun and comin
    they creep and flee wi rowth o bummin.

    Jimmy's skerred, an that's the truth,
    the puir man nearly hits the roof.
    "Ouch!" wan gets him in the neck,
320 an therr's anuther, at his leg.
    Up an doon, an roon aboot,
    cloacks come buzzin, fleein oot.

    Here peer Tammie – tak a sicht!
    Lowpin oot o's bed in fricht.
325 "Gweeshtins!" – Een fae's craig he cleeks,
    syne anidder sclims his breeks!
    Here an yont the clocks is comin,
    creepin, fleein, birlin, bummin.

    Dan hit isna raelly lang,
    fir he loups up wi a spang.
325 "Ooch", der een apo his craig,
    in his sark an up his leg.
    Shön da mird's aa owre da plaess,
    arlin, fleein wi lood bizz.

Onkel Fritz in dieser Not,	And, despairing, Uncle Fred
330 Haut und trampelt alles tot.	330 beats and stamps till all are dead.

| Guckste wohl! Jetzt ist's vorbei | "There you are – now let me be!" |
| Mit der Käferkrabbelei!! | Ended is his misery. |

Onkel Fritz hat wieder Ruh	Uncle Fred soon shuts his eyes,
Und macht seine Augen zu. –	peacefully asleep he lies.
335 Dieses war der fünfte Streich,	335 That concludes the fifth bad deed –
Doch der sechste folgt sogleich.	there are more, as you shall read.

stottin aff the waalls wor they,
hunnords deyin i this way.
Hwen nayin's left ti massacree,
Unkil mops ees broo wi glee,
335 hes a tot, myakes up ees nest,
saftly lays ees heed ti rest ...
"A treyimph!" crey the lissnin paior,
"huz cud gan on for ivvor maior!"

Uncle Frank is in a borl,
330 thumps them ti the aw'er worl.
Dead the clocks is every one,
deed their crawlin days is done!
Uncle Frank sleeps leck a chile
knowin that he's safe the while.
335 That's the skitthers' fith bad deed –
here's the sikth, jus tick a read.

Uncle Jock in his dire steid
330 clowts and stramps the hale lot deid.
Tak ye tent hou he can sattle
aa thae creepie-crawlie cattle!
Uncle Jock cam aff the best,
steeked his een and lay at rest.
335 Tellin o the fift tale's dune –
saxt yin follies richt ahin.

Uncle James, near aff his heid,
swipes an blooters till thur deid.
325 See noo, that's them aw kaput –
nae merr beetles crawlin oot!
Uncle James at last calms doon,
an faws asleep agrain, rale soon.
That wis Five, an noo comes nict –
330 as ye'd expeck, Terr Number Six.

Uncle Tam in fleysome dreid
330 dunts an dirds em aa tae deid.
Here a sicht at's fine an rare—
noo the golochs crowl nae mair.
Peace again, an Uncle Tam
steeks his een as quaet's a lamb.
335 Pliskie Nummer Five wes yon –
tae the neist we'se noo meeve on.

Uncle Olly, frushin, laid
330 fae him, fir da clocks wis dead.
Yiss, doo sees der nae mair boags
noo at sprickles, scarts or oags.
Uncle eence mair steeks his een,
snores anaeth da coonterpeen.
335 Plunkie five is here abön –
Bit da sixt een follows shön.

SECHSTER STREICH   EPISODE SIX

In der schönen Osterzeit,   Easter is a happy season
Wenn die frommen Bäckersleut,   when good pastry-cooks have reason
Viele süße Zuckersachen   to prepare and knead and bake
340 Backen und zurechtemachen,   340 every sort of bun and cake.
Wünschten Max und Moritz auch   Sugar, spice and all things sweet
Sich so etwas zum Gebrauch. —   Mac and Murray loved to eat.

Doch der Bäcker, mit Bedacht,   Here the Baker has a key
Hat des Backhaus zugemacht.   and he locks his bakery;

345 Also, will hier einer stehlen,   345 so to get into the shop
Muß er durch den Schlot sich quälen. —   one must squeeze in from the top.

Sixt Skeylaak

Eastor noo, wi aal its fun,
340 pyaist egg gayim an het crass bun;
bakstors, fu o wark an caior,
myaikin cyakes an sweetmeats raior.
Moas an Meyk o coorse hed plans –
baith o them hed yeuky hans.
345 But the bakstor'd larnt lang seyn
thit ees guddies temptid feyne;
kept ees bakhoose teyght's a drum –
yin lane loop-hwole, doon the lum.

Sikth Thrick

At Easther time, the worl biz ree;
dacint bakers diz feel free,
mick all kines o tasty bakes
340 jam tarts, biscuits, buns an cakes.
Mack an Maurice see the thrait,
good things they wʌd leck ti ate,
Still the baker, damned as but,
locks his dure as tight as gut.
345 Wan as wants ti stale mus come
tight as mordher through the lum.

Saxt Ploy

Eastertide's a braw time when
pious kirk-gaun baxter men
look the graith they need to bake
340 monie a tasty sugar-cake.
Dod and Davie had a mind
t'ettle something o that kind.
But the baxter, wycelike man
maks the bake-hous safe's he can.
345 Stealin in a chiel wad need
to sprauchle throu the chimley-heid.

Sixth Terr

Easter's aye a happy time,
when bakers, gude folk, dae a line
in Easter eggs, an buns an cake –
aw the sweet things they kin make.
335 Matt an Malkie, shure enough,
hiv thur eyes oan aw thon stuff.
The baker, bit, he knows the score,
double-loacks the bakehoose door.
If they want tae knock a cake,
340 the lum's the road they'll need tae take.

Sixt Pliskie

In the blyesome days o Pace,
fin the byaakers, fou o grace,
crumpy succar biscuits byaaks,
340 an a haep of teethsome cyaaks,
Mac an Matthy thocht ey'd like
tee, tae get a cheerie pyke.
But the byaaker's faar ower sleekit:
Here the byaakhoose door he's steekit!
345 Sae, gin ony thief wad come,
nae wey in – but doon the lum.

Plunkie Six

Aester is a time fir joy,
whin maist bakers, man an boy,
wirks da leelang day ta bake
340 curny buns an slabs o cake.
Jarm an Jeemsie wiss ta aet
some o dis fine lookin maet.
Bit da baker, nae föl he,
steeks da bakehoose wi da key.
345 Der jöst wan wye tieves can come –
dat's wi reeslin doon da lum.

Ratsch!! – Da kommen die zwei Knaben Durch den Schornstein, schwarz wie Raben.	Swish! And through the chimney-stack swoop the boys completely black.

Puffl!! – Sie fallen in die Kist,
350 Wo das Mehl darinnen ist.

Da! Nun sind sie alle beide
Rund herum so weiß wie Kreide.

Plop! They promptly come to rest
350 right inside the flour-chest.

Here you see them as they walk
both are white, as white as chalk.

Sa, bi shoo*r*, on feeistin bund,
350 Meyk un Moas the lane gyate fund.
Doon thi cum an blinly tweest
plump inti the floowor keest;
noo thor wheyte f*r*um heed ti toa,
but thor een aa*r*e aal aglow,

Whoosh, bedad here comes the two
black as ravens down the flue.
Poof! They're in the ark o male
350 dipped in flour from head ti tail:
See them crawl out from the bax
white as any strake o flax.

Doun the lum the laddies faa
gettin black as onie craw.
Fuff! Intil the kist they clour
350 whar the baxter keeps his flour.
Owre the bake-hous flair they walk
lookin baith as white as chalk.

Crash! right doon the chimney faws
thon bad boays as black as craws,
an whoosh! arrive wi clouds a stoor,
in a big boax fulla floor –
345 So's when they get up an walk,
heid tae toe thur white as chalk.

Clash! – an doon the loonies faa,
oot the chimley, black's a craa.
Ere a mael-kist lang an wide:
350 Poof! – ey tummle richt inside.
See the pair o skypels noo:
Black's a craa? – Na, fite's a doo!

Wi a dunt da twa boys faas
trow da shimley, black as craas.
Boof! Da scunners dan salist
350 richt athin da aald floor kist.
Trivlin owre da flör dey waalk,
dey ir noo as white as chaalk.

Aber schon mit viel Vergnügen
Sehen sie die Brezeln liegen.

Full of joy they soon espy
lovely pretzels, way up high.

355 Knacks!! – Da bricht der Stuhl entzwei;
Schwapp!! – Da liegen sie im Brei.

355 Crack! The chair breaks – here they go
slap! into the sticky dough.

355 seein nowt aroond but cyake,
shelf on shelf, fo them ti tyake.
On a chaior thi shaapish lowp –
as it breks thi shaapor cowp,

On a shelf they spy some things,
a thray o lovely gravy-rings!
355 Crash! The chair's broke! Down they go
headlong in a throkh o dough –

Joyfully the laddies spy
whar the crusty breid's pit by.
355 Crack! The chair is broke in twa,
in the mixin-troch they faa,

Delightet noo, they spoat a treat,
a shelf wi sticky buns tae eat.
Crack! thur cherr collapses, through –
350 splat! thur stretcht oot in the dough.

Fit reck ey, tho – seen ey're blye,
seein far the cyaakies lie.
355 Crack! The creepie braks in twaa!
Flaff! amo the daigh ey faa!

Bit dey skrime shön i da dim
fancy cookies – nyim, nyim, nyim!
355 Craack! Da shair noo gings in soe.
Platsh! Dey laand ita da dough.

Ganz von Kuchenteig umhüllt
Stehn sie da als Jammerbild. –

Bathed in batter stand the pair
in a posture of despair.

Gleich erscheint der Meister Bäcker
360 Und bemerkt die Zuckerlecker.

Eins, zwei, drei! – eh man's gedacht,
Sind zwei Brote draus gemacht.

Master Baker hears some noise,
360 recognises both the boys,

one, two, three – no word is said –
and they're kneaded into bread.

streyght inti sum waitin duff –
360 clagged thi helpliss i the stuff!
Bakstor Taam, haard on the hoowor,
laands – an eys the syut an floowor –
Spleet-splat, fleep-flap, twee loaves myed –
pleep-plop, int' the yuvvin spyed!

covered wi the sticky paste
stan leck ornaments o waste.
Soon the baker comes an sees
360 greedy gorbs caked till a frieze.
Wan, two, three, the baker scuttles
quick as light – two long bread shuttles.

streaks o miserie in a fix
happit in the gouie mix.
Ben the hous the baxter warsles,
360 sees thir unco sweetie-morsels.
Yin, twa, three! And quick as thocht
'til twa fancy loafs they're wrocht.

Therr they staun, a sorry sight,
batter-coated, if ye like.
Straight away, the baker's therr,
sees thon jammy-fingered perr –
355 Wan, two! afore ye've time tae blink,
he's made thum intae loafs, jis think!

Sosst wi daigh fae heid til tae –
fegs, ey're sairie sichts o wae
In rins byaaker noo in haste,
360 sees the sweet-teeths sclatched wi paste.
Een-twaa-three –an in a blenk,
twaa wee laifies on the benk.

Staandin clatched fae head ta tae,
dey, I'se warn, ir braaly wae.
In da mester baker pins,
360 he will sort dem fir der sins.
Didna dey get a forsmo,
whin he rowed dem i da dough!

In dem Ofen glüht es noch –
Ruff!! – damit ins Ofenloch!

Look, the oven is still hot,
in they go the wicked lot!

365 Ruff!! – man zieht sie aus der Glut –
Denn nun sind sie braun und gut. –

– Jeder denkt „die sind perdü!"
Aber nein! – noch leben sie! –

365 Here they come now, tumbling down,
ready baked, both crisp and brown.

You must think their end is near –
no indeed, they are still here!

365 Sumteyme lator, oot thi cum,
    broon an creesp an smoakin – yum!
    Taam smeyles caz thor nowt but dust,
    but ee's wrang caz, neath the crust,
    Meyk an Moas aare livin weel,
370 chowin hwoales bi which thi steal,

    Hear, the oven's hot as hell
    shove them in an bake them well.
365 Wiff! They're pʌlled out from the hate
    nice an brown an good till ate.
    Don't you think they've kicked the bucket?
    They're not dead allo they lʌk it!

    Oven nou is lowin reid,
    steeks them in wi muckle speed,
365 draws them out when he can see
    loafs are cookit to a T.
    Ilk yin thinks, "Weel that was it!"
    Naw! The lads are no deid yit!

    The oven's stull hoat. gaun great –
    wheech! he shoves thum in tae bake,
    then wheech! again, afore they burn,
360 He whups thum oot, done tae a turn.
    That's them finisht, oot the gemme,
    ivrybuddy thinks – no them.

    In the een the quile's a-lowe –
    Wheech! – he staps em in the howe.
365 Wheech! – he pous em fae the haet,
    broon an fine eneuch tae aet!
    Seer, ye'd think, ey're by wi't noo?
    Na, ey're livin yet, A trou!

    I da ov'n der still heat coll.
    Whoof! He bangs dem i da holl.
365 Whoof! Dey're draan oot fae da glöd –
    Yea, da baker's wark is göd.
    Tinks doo at der end is near?
    Na, der life yit i dis pair!

Knusper, knasper! – wie zwei Mäuse
370 Fressen sie durch das Gehäuse;

Crunch and crackle, watch them well,
370 nibble through their crusty shell.

Und der Meister Bäcker schrie:
„Achherrje! da laufen sie!!" –

And the Baker in surprise,
"Dear oh dear, they're off!" he cries.

Dieses war der sechste Streich,
Doch der letzte folgt sogleich.

That concludes the sixth bad deed –
there are more as you shall read.

unbikent an underthoom,
oot the loaves an oot the rum,
nivvor knaan ti move sa fast,
spottid ownly at the last.
375 "Narra squeak!" the lads agreed –
bleynd tiv it as waarnin rede.

Crummle, crummle leck a screw
370 through the pasthry cruss they chew.
Baker roars, near aff his head:
"God, them baygles shʌd be dead!"
That's the cuchees' sikth bad ack –
fate is close behine their back.

Nibble, nibble, like twa mousis
370 eat their wey out o their housis.
Baxter cried at what he saw:
"Dagont lads hae rin awa!"
Tellin o the saxt tale's dune –
hinmaist follies richt ahin.

Nibble, nibble – lik two mice,
they stert tae eat thur crust – it's nice!
365 The baker shouts, his mooth agape,
"Goad Almighty, thuv escaped!"
That's the Number Six Terr past –
noo here foallies Terr the Last.

Moupie-mappie – jist lik moosies,
370 ramshin throu eir crumpy hoosies!
"Deil be lickit! Ey're escapin" –
Byaaker gowls – "tae dee mair japin!"
Pliskie Nummer Six wes yon –
tae the last we'se noo meeve on.

Laek twa mice dey pick an showe,
370 fir da crust is aeten trow.
Dan we hear da baker reein:
"O my gorie, see dem fleein!"
Plunkie six is here abön –
bit da hidmaist follows shön.

LETZTER STREICH   EPISODE SEVEN

375   Max und Moritz, wehe euch!   375   Mac and Murray, now look out!
     Jetzt kommt euer letzter Streich! –   This shall be your final bout!

Wozu müssen auch die beiden   Where's the sense and where the gain
Löcher in die Säcke schneiden?? –   cutting holes in sacks of grain?

    – Seht, da trägt der Bauer Mecke   Look, the farmer takes his sack
380   Einen seiner Maltersäcke. –   380   and he slings it on his back.

    Aber kaum daß er von hinnen,   As he leaves and starts to go
    Fängt das Korn schon an zu rinnen.   so the corn begins to flow.

Sivinth Skeylaak

Teyme bi then waas *r*innin oot
fo the heedstrang paior, nee doobt,
but the feckliss chanced thor luck
380 i the baarn o Faamor Muck,
hackin hwoales in aal ees poaks,
sartin 'twaas the best o joaks.
But thor still theor hwin ee laands,
heykes a poak up in ees hands,

Hinmaist Ploy

375 Dod and Davie, walawae!
Here's the last ploy that ye'll play.
What for wale amang your jokes
cuttin holes in aa the pokes?
See, here comes auld Fermer Broun
380 humphin secks o corn aroun.
Barely has he turned about
nor the corn is skailin out.

Last Pliskie

375 Mac an Matthy, lack the day!
Iss ull ploy's the last ye'll play!
Fit for man ey cut yon haggies
in the fermer's stappit baggies?
In comes Mains, an aff the fleer
380 hysts a muckle bag o bere.
But twaa steps he disna win,
or it's stertin oot tae rin.

Las Thrick

375 Mack an Maurice, howl yir cup!
Yir las thrick is comin up.
Why mus these two sleekid lags
cut them slashes in the bags?
Lʌk! the farmer lifts the sack
380 for ti carry on his back.
Soon as he begins ti clime
out runs corn leck it was lime.

Last Terr

Matt an Malkie, noo, take kerr!
370 This is it, yir final terr!
Whit's gaun oan wi they two brats,
cuttin holes in coarn sacks?
See, therr's puir auld Fermer Mac,
humphin wan oot owre his back.
375 He disnae even make the door,
doon the coarn sterts tae pour.

Hidmaist Plunkie

375 Jarm an Jeemsie, noo tak vaar!
Your neist ploy will ging owre far!
Whitwye dö dey hae ta spölli
göd fock's coarnsecks wi a tully?
Crofter Magnie we see here,
380 on his back a seck o bere.
Whin he gings ta stramp awa,
coarn in doontöm starts ta faa.

Und verwundert steht und spricht er:
„Zapperment! Dat Ding werd lichter!"

Puzzled by his light-weight load,
he exclaims: "Well, I'll be blowed!"

385 Hei! Da sieht er voller Freude
      Max und Moritz im Getreide.

      Rabs!! – in seinen großen Sack
      Schaufelt er das Lumpenpack.

385 "There they are the ruddy boys!"
      It's a sight that he enjoys.

      Quick, into the great, big sack,
      in goes Murray, in goes Mac.

385 stumps awaa an – nee yin's fyul –
tweegs ees poak is faar frum fyull.
Sley ees een prey heydy-plyaces,
siun ee speys twee weel-kent fyaces.
Wi a lang an suddint streyde,
390 sweeps ee baith lads up inseyde!

All at onct he stans there shoutin:
"Dang mi sowl! The bag is spoutin."
385 Then his heart swells wi delight:
he's marked the gʌlpins in his sight.
Quick! He opens wide his sack
shoves them in, then piggy-back!

Stoppit, ferlie-full, and peched:
"Blastit seck is lossin wecht!"
385 Sees wi pleisure the forforn
twasome dernin in the corn.
"Got ye!" There and than, by heck,
Shools the skellums in the seck.

Mac jis cannae take it in:
"Michty me! This bag's gat thin!"
Ha! he spoats thum wi a smile,
380 Matt an Malkie in the pile.
Wheech! he grabs thon scallywags,
shoves thum smartly in a bag.

Mains staans stull: "A maun be dreamin!
Whit's gaun oan! The dag thing's teemin!"
385 Fit he sees now maks him fain –
Mac an Matthy 'mo the grain.
In the muckle bag he sheels
wi a wheech the twaa wee deils!

Bröls he as da fraacht gets licht:
"Dwine dis seck, shöy isnö töicht!"
385 Wisna he da blyde ta see
Jarm an Jeemsie, hit's nae lee!
Whoosh! Ita his seck da twa
oolets baith gings headicraa.

Max und Moritz wird es schwüle,
390 Denn nun geht es nach der Mühle. –

Now the naughty boys feel ill
390 for the path leads to the mill.

„Meister Müller, he, heran!
Mahl er das, so schnell er kann!"

„Her damit!!" – Und in den Trichter
Schüttelt er die Bösewichter. –

"Hi there, Miller! Grind this lot,
do it quick and on the spot!"

"Right you are!" And through the funnel
go the rascals down the tunnel.

Meyk an Moas misdoot thor fyate
as thi sweeng tiv Aad Muck's gyait;
mair sae hwin thi heor ees veyce,
then the Milnor's nyame a preyce!
395 Sweesh! Baith oauts an stowwaways
sleethors diun the shutt an gais

Mack an Maurice hez their fears
390 ti the mill the farmer steers.
"Misther Miller, pay me heed.
Grine me this up wi all speed."
In they go an each wee brute
whizzes down the grin'in shute.

Dod and Davie fecht for air;
390 to the mill he humphs the pair.
"Maister Miller, my gweed man,
grind this corn as quick's ye can."
"Gie it me!" And in the happer
cowps the rascals for the clapper.

Matt an Malkie feel right ill,
that's them gaun tae the mill –
385 "Maister Miller, are ye there?
Grind these up, an dinna spare!
In ye go!" an doon the hopper,
Matt an Malkie come a cropper.

Mac an Matthy 'gin tae fear,
390 for the mull's noo unco near.
"Muller! Haw, whaur urr ye, man!
Grunn this up as fast's ye can!"
"Here wi't than!" – an in the happer
seen the rascals get a crapper!

Jarm an Jeemsie noo dreed ill,
390 fir he taks dem ta da mill.
"Mester miller, heest dee, man,
Grind doo dis, as shön's doo can!"
"Reck dem owre." An dan he heaves
doon da happer wir twa tieves.

395 Rickeracke! Rickeracke!
     Geht die Mühle mit Geknacke.

395 Hear the mill-stones grind and squeak,
     rattle, rattle, crack and creak.

Hier kann man sie noch erblicken
Fein geschroten und in Stücken.

See, the boys may still be found,
bits and pieces, finely ground.

    Doch sogleich verzehret sie
400 Meister Müllers Federvieh.

    But the Miller's ducks devour
400 all that's left, in half an hour.

heltor-skeltor ti be br*u*st
twixt the styanes an torned ti dust.
Aad Muck mused thior i the stoowor:
400 Meyk an Moas lay on the floowor;
yince see pr*o*od, noo smeethors smaa,
baiyit fo ducks an gissies br*a*a.

395 Gruntin, grumlin, grines the stones
flesh an hair an teeth an bones.
Ach, the gossoons fate was shure
Groun ti bits upon the flure!
Till the millers' ducks wi joy
400 gobbled up them lumps o boy.

395 Nicketie-nacketie nicketie-nack
stounds the mill wi a clicketie-clack.
Nou ye wadna ken the lads
weel-grund down and champed to blads.
Maister Miller's feathered foolies
400 gobble up the tasty moolies.

Rickle-rackle! that's the sound,
390 thon bad boays makes gettin ground.
See thum efter lyin therr,
wee dauds sprinkled owre the flerr;
then up comes the Miller's ducks,
an disappear thum doon thur guts!

395 Wi a creakin, crackin soon
turns the mull-wheel roon an roon.
Ay eenou ey're stull tae see,
aa grunn doon tae nirlies wee,
but ey're golloped up in haste –
400 Mullart's jeukies hae a faest.

395 Lood da wheels noo snyirks an clumps,
hear da millstane as he crumps!
We can still mak oot dis pair,
bit da skroil is shön nae mair,
caas da miller's deuks noo sprits
400 fir ta glaep doon aa da bits.

SCHLUSS

Als man dies im Dorf erfuhr,
War von Trauer keine Spur. –
– Witwe Bolte, mild und weich,
Sprach: „Sieh da, ich dacht es gleich!" –
405 – „Ja ja ja" rief Meister Böck –
„Bosheit ist kein Lebenszweck!" –
– Drauf so sprach Herr Lehrer Lämpel:
„Dies ist wieder ein Exempel!" –
– „Freilich!" meint der Zuckerbäcker –
410 „Warum ist der Mensch so lecker?!" –

EPILOGUE

When the news reached farm and city,
there was not a trace of pity.
Mistress Bold, with gentle touch,
said: "Ah well, I thought as much!"
405 Master Buck remarked: "Quite, quite!
Life should not be full of spite!"
Whereupon good Master Lample
called it: "Just one more example!"
And the Baker mused: "Indeed,
410 why must man indulge in greed?"

THE MORRIL O THE TYALE

Hwen the village, chucklin grim,
Patcht up hwaat'd happind thim,
405 Widda Boola sayd, "Yi see,
Sum sic end waas boond ti be."
Seppy Gryace sayd, "Ey, eggs hatch;
Leyves o mischif, deeths ti match."
Biffy Laasun sayd, "Tck-tck –
410 Kennin Reet frum Wrang's the treeck."
Bakstor Tam laaft fit ti brust:
"Ey, but shaapor larnt, Aa trust!"

THE EN

In the village not wan soun
nor wan sigh o grief was foun.
Wida Kelly talkin low
knowed that they wʌd come ti woe.
405 "Served them right," Buck ti the wife:
"Mischief's not the aim o life."
Sadly Sample said: "Yi know
these things ony goes ti show."
Baker said: "A'll tell yi thrue
410 leckin sweets can bring yi rue."

TAIL PIECE

When the news ran throu the toun
fient a tear was latten doun.
Weeda Bauld, o gentie mind,
"Expeckit something o the kind."
405 "Ay, ay, ay," cried Goat the Teyler,
"badness is o life the speyler."
Up then spak the Dominie:
"The warning's there for all to see!"
The Baxter, kneddin at his pastry,
410 wonnert: "What maks man sae tasty?"

395 Well, when people goat tae hear,
naebdy shed a single tear.
Widda Blooter, puir auld wummin,
says, "Oh ay, Ah seen it comin."
"Ay, that's right," says Tailor Boke,
400 life jist isnae wan long joke."
Teacher Lampwick shook his heid,
"Here's a lesson now indeed!"
"Definately," says the baker,
"jammy fingers gets ye naewherr."

EPILOG

Fin fock kent the tragedie,
deil a tear in ony ee.
For the douce aal weeda umman
said: "Aye, fine A saa it comin!"
405 "Aye, aye, aye!" criet Maister Gait,
"Dinna gang a skypel's gate!"
Lintie, Maister o the Squeel,
said: "The moral – think on't weel!"
An the byaaker said: "Young geeties
410 sudna be sae keen on sweeties!"

FEENISH

Whin dey heard da news dat day,
fock, I doot, wis far fae wae.
Weedow Baald, blyde spaekin wife,
said: "Is dat no jöst laek life?"
405 Mester Lamb toucht: "Yis, yis, yis,
Boys sood keep fae ploys laek dis."
Lö noo weel ta teacher Tait:
"Ill is whaat aa bairns sood hate."
"Yea", said noo da mester baker,
410 "Staelin cake jöst maks me siccar!"

– Selbst der gute Onkel Fritze
Sprach: „Das kommt von dumme Witze!" –
– Doch der brave Bauersmann
Dachte: „Wat geiht meck dat an?!" –
415 – Kurz, im ganzen Dorf herum
Ging ein freudiges Gebrumm:
„Gott sei Dank! Nun ist's vorbei
Mit der Übeltäterei!!"

Even Uncle Frederick spoke:
"Never play a foolish joke!"
But the simple farmer, he
thought: "Bain't nowt to do wi' me!"
415 Everyone around, in brief,
uttered words of great relief.
"God be praised! We're free at last! –
Wicked deeds are of the past!"

Glad bireaved aad Unkil shrugs:
"Cums o gowkeesh treecks, ye bugs!"
415 As fa reed-fyaced Faamor Muck,
Ee riched forra straa ti suck ...
Ivribody hed yin thowt,
As thi, gigglin, sorcht an sowght –
Nat ti feynd thi meesin paior,
420 But ti myek shoor thi waarn't thior.

Even Uncle Frank towl folks:
"See what comes o crackin jokes."
Farmer John said: "Och, yir head!
Dizn't bo'er me they're dead."
415 Through the place, a howl there went,
wan long sigh o sweet content.
"Praise be God! The place is free
of their sleekid foolery!"

Spak up Uncle Jock himsel:
"Sic a pair o gomerel!"
Fermer Broun was quate a wee,
syne thocht: "Fat's 'at t' dee wi me?"
415 Deed! Cam rummlin throu the toun
sic a blydesome merry soun:
"God be thanked! We're quat o boys
wi their harum-scarum ploys!"

405 Even Uncle James admits,
"serves thum right, thur stchupit tricks.
Therr's an end tae aw thur jokin."
The fermer couldnae gie a doacken.
Pit it briefly, shoart an sweet,
410 shouts wis heard in ivry street,
"Goad be thankt, that's owre an done,
nae merr roatten tricks fur fun!"

Uncle Tam, sae aft begeckit,
said: "It's jist as A expeckit!"
Mains, the fermer, fine an smert,
thocht: "Hit wullnae brak ma hert!"
415 Ne'er a cheil in aa the clachan
but wes crackin blye an lachin:
"Losh be thankit! Noo nae mair
deeds o vrang fae yon ull pair!"

Even göd aald uncle Olly
said: "Dis comes fae siclaek foally."
Bit da eident crofter swör:
"Gori, soar a peel I työr!"
415 Sae doo sees, in ev'ry hoose
fock said, blyde an odious croose:
"Göd be tankit, hit's by noo,
aa da tricks an hubbleskyoo!"

MAX AN MARRIS

two rude bway,
seven diffrant badness weh dem do,
translated into Jamaican Creole
by Jean D'Costa

MAKS ƐN MƆRIS

Stori bɔt tu raskɛl bɔbɔ pan sɛvin trik,
na Frɛdi Jons translet am to Krio vas.

Lissen now, som pickney bad:
Two bway rude so tell dem mad!
All me talk a suo-so truut:
Max an Marris in dem yout
5 neva stody, troble teacha,
neva pay no mine to preacha.
Dem so fiesty in dem ways
fi-dem mout should wash wid Jeyes.
Coke-nat saafa dan dem head
10 school mean notten to de dread.
Was'e a time fi stody book
when rudeness yuh a look.
School an church a ignarance
when mango-time bring yuh chance.
15 Climb tree tief aringe an plom –
bot in school dem deaf an domb.
All dem good fa is fi tease
who som eva dem mine please.
Time, yuh know, langa dan ruop,
20 sipple muor dan washin suop.
Koo de pickcha an de verse
weh dem gaan fram bad to worse.

BADNESS NOMBA WAN

Plenty people mine dem fowl,
ron weh mangoose, hawk, an owl.
25 Fos ting, fowl-hegg good fi h'eat,
bwail or fry-op nice wid meat.
Nex ting, chicken friggisee
mek mout-waata ron like sea.
When yuh waan yuh pilla saaf
30 use de fedda weh plock aaf,
fedda mek op nice, waam bed
fi-yuh res yuh tired head.
See de pickcha in de book:
A so Mada Bolt did look.
35 She did keep tree nice-nice en
an wan roosta rule de pen.

PRIFES

A, wi kin rid plɛnti tin
ɔ yɛri bɔt bad pikin!
Luk lɛk Maks ɛn Mɔris so
we, fɔ mek dɛn tink ɔ sho
5 se dɛm nɔ kɔmɔt na waf,
nɔ bisin, bɔt kin jɛs laf
ɛn mek jok bɔt aw dɛm tan
to dɛm sɛf sɛf gud gud wan.
Fɔ ple raskɛl na swit tin,
10 tɔmɛnt bist ɛn tiz pɔsin,
tif pia, plɔm ɛn apul
ɛn ɛnjɔy dɛnsɛf bɛlful –
ɔl dis bɛtɛ pas sidɔm
saful wan, nɔ shek, nɔ fɔm
15 na chia na chɔch ɔ skul
ɛn ɔl dis nɔ gɛt nɔ rul.
Bɔt o ya, o ya, o ya,
wɛn a luk di rizɔlt, a!
Maks ɛn Mɔris sɔfa ɛl.
20 So, dɛm bad trik ɛn raskɛl
ɔl de na ya na drɔin
ɛn de dɔng sɛf na raytin.

FƆS TRIK

Uman dɛm we de mɛn fɔl
kin lebɔ fɔ kip dɛn ɔl.
25 Wan, bikɔs ɔl man no se
eg na tin we fɔl kin le.
Tu, bikɔs, wan wan tɛm so,
ros chikin fayn fɔ it o.
Tri, man kin tek dɛm fɛda
30 fɔ mek kushin ɛn pila.
Pipul lɛk dɛm bed fɔ wam
we na nɛt slip tɛm dɔn kam.
Luk lɛk wido Bolt na ya,
di mami sɛf lɛk kɔba.
35 Dis mami bin gɛt tri ɛn
ɛn sɛf wan prawd kak wit dɛm.

TAR AN TAVA

Pikin i tori wei i gɛt sɛvɛn pat,
Loreto Todd bin putam fɔ pijin.

MAX NA MORITZ

stori bilong tupela manki.
Wilhelm Busch i bin raitim lonk tok Siaman,
Don Laycock i bin tanim lonk tok Pisin

Fɔs Ting

A! Di tori dɛm di tɔk
fɔ pikin wei du bad wɔk.
Jɔs laik dis tu Tar an Tava
wei soso sabi fain palava.
5   Dɛm nɛva trai fɔ lisɛn wɛl
fɔ gud ting wei man di tɛl.
No, dɛm sabi laf an plei
hambak pipul ɛni dei,
soso trɔng-hɛd fɔ dɛm skul,
10 dis pikim dɛm laik fɔ ful.
Man dei so, i bɛnbɛn smɔl,
laik fɔ glad i sɛf ɔl ɔl,
wɔri man, ɔ naknak bif
laik fɔ plei, fɔ jok, fɔ tif.
15 Diskain ting i isi pas
sidɔng fɔ skul ɔ sing fɔ Mas.
Bɔt helele! a tɔk fɔ tru
di bad wei Tar an Tava du.
Wuna lisɛn fɔ di kɔni
20 Dis tu pikin tink sei fɔni.
Di tori dei fɔ dis ma buk
mek wi ɔl bigin fɔ luk.

Nɔmba Wan Kɔni

Plenti pipul laik fɔ gɛt
faul dɛm wei na gud-lɔk bɛt.
25 Fɔs fɔsika dɛm gif ek,
pei wi fɔ di pen wi tek.
Dɛn a shua sei ɔl man gri
faul dɛm fain fɔ chɔp fɔ wi,
wɛn wi fit fɔ hapi taim
30 tekam, kukam, laikam fain.
Agɛn wi sabi yus dɛm feda
wɔm wi skin fɔ badbad weda.
Mek wi tɔk fɔ Mami Bol
wei nɛva laik fɔ slip fɔ kol.
35 Mami Bol gɛt tri smɔl hɛn
an wan man faul i gɛt agɛn.

Long Rida

Pasin bilong manki i olsem:
long olkain trik i no ken sem.
Ol i hambak, ol i kranki.
Nau mi stori long tupela manki,
5   Max na Moritz, ol i kolim.
Tupela i no save holim
gutpela tingting bilong ol tisa;
tupela i save lap long misa,
tok bilas long meriman,
10 hambak nabaut long evriwan.
Wonem samting man i gat,
tupela i stilim olsem rat;
tinmit, banana, wonem samting,
tupela i save tekim nating.
15 Tupela i no go long skul,
mekim pasin bladiful. –
Tasol wantok, yu mas sori
long pinis bilong dispela stori,
taim Max na Moritz tupela i dai,
20 ating, pren, bai yu ken krai.
Nau yu ritim stori long dispela buk
na long ol piksa yu ken lukluk.

Trik Namba Wan

Planti man long planti hap
kakaruk i gat i stap,
25 olsem long tripela risin
ol i lukautim dispela pisin:
Nambawan: bilong ol kiau
ol kakaruk i siutim nau.
Nambatu: ol mit bilong kakaruk
30 i gutpela kaikai na gutpela sup.
Na pulimapim pilo long gras,
o wokim matres, i narapela as.
Na meri Bolte i no sem
long laik long mekim olsem.
35 Kakaruk i ron long san
i tripela meri na wanpela man.

Max an Marris try fi fine
som tiefin plan in dem mine:
Dem kot fuor small piece a bread
40 lickle like yuh finga-head,
jine de piece wid 'tring well tight,
like Nancy-web spin a night;
tie i craas-way wid som caad,
set i in de lady yaad.
45 Cack see, an im bawl out loud:
"Kukuruu!" fi call de crowd,
fa troo out de whole a life
cack live good wid all im wife.
All a dem did fly an ron
50 com get piece befuor i don.
When dem don nyam aaf de bread
non a dem kyan move dem head.
Roun an roun dem haul an pull
tell de neck dem 'tretch out full.
55 Dem a fight an fight an coss:
every secan mek i woss.
Dem a flatta in de h'air,
fedda flyin everywhere,
tell wan dry tree-limb ketch dem,
60 draw dem neck tight an 'tretch dem.
Frighten tek dem, an dem bawl
while de neck dem lang out tall.
Wan muor hegg each wan did lay,
den dem spirit pass away!
65 Mada Bolt inside in bed
hear de fowl-dem bawl fi dead;
kuol-sweat wash ar every limb,
when she look, ar yeye ton dim.
"Lawd-a-massy! Puor me gyal!
70 Fi-me luck no good at all!
Eye-waata com! All me fowl
heng up dead pan tree like owl!"
Das de woss day in ar life,
bot she get de kitchen knife,
75 so kot de bady fram de tree
an in deat' she set dem free.
To ar ouse she walk go slow,
fa dis sarrow bring ar low.
Dis a de fos badness: quick –
80 nex wan com like faya-stick.

Badness Nomba Two

Afta de bad feelins pass
Mada Bolt decide de laas
respeck she kyan give
dem what neva muor wi live
85 a fi ruos dem good an sweet
when she feel a mine fi eat.

So, Maks ɛn Mɔris wan de
tink us raskɛl gem fɔ ple.
As di tin kam na dɛm ed
40 kwik, wan, tu, tri dɛm kɔt bred
fo pis – smɔl, smɔl wan dɛm ɔl,
finga sayz na so dɛm smɔl.
Dɛm tay dɛm, a dɛm wikɛd!
Wan pis bred ɛng dɔng wan trɛd,
45 dɛn, dɛm fɛn di mami yad,
put dɛm de ɛn kip dɛm gyad.
As di kak kin si di bred
na im o; i tret im ed
ɛn kro "kokorioko!"
50 Na di ɛn dɛm i kɔl so.
Tak, tak, tak, tak, luk dɛm de
kak ɛn ɛn de swɛla we.
Sun na im dɛm sɛf kam si
say nɔ de fɔ mek dɛm fri.
55 ɔp ɛn dɔng ɛn lɛft ɛn rayt
rɔn so te bɔt, o, ples tayt.
Dɛm jomp ɔp fɔ flay kɔmɔt,
A, dis wahala ful mɔt!
O ya Gɔd! Dɛm ɛng de swing
60 na wan branch we insɛf ling.
ɛn dɛm nɛk jɛs de langa
as dɛm ala de tranga,
tɛl dɛm le dɛm eg bay fos
na im dɛm giv ɔp di gos.
65 Mami Bolt frɔm rayt insay
na im bed yɛri di kray.
I sɔspɛkt se tin dɔn bi
so i kam na do fɔ si;
a, di tin we im yay si
70 mek wata rɔn yay pan mi!
"Ɔl mi op ɛn dizaya,
ɔl mi drim na dis dunya!"
Sɔri so na im i bi
ɛn kɔt dɔng dɛm fɔl bɔdi
75 mek dɛm nɔ lɛf aw dɛm tan.
Dɛn i luk dɛm sɔri wan,
i fil am bɔt i nɔ sho,
nɔ se fing bɔt i jɛs go.
Dis na bin di fɔs bad trik
80 ɛn di sɛkɛn apin kwik.

Sɛkɛn Trik

Di gud mami nɛks mɔnin
tray kam to, ɛn di bɛs tin
we i tink se i fɔ du
fɔ di rɛspɛkt we dɛm dyu,
85 na fɔ it di po fɔl dɛm
we dɔn day bifo dɛm tɛm

Tar an Tava dɛm hɛd klia,
dis tu boi dɛm no di fia.
Kwik kwik so dɛm gɛt sɔm yam,
40   kɔtam, kukam, bringam kam.
Yam i smɔl i pas njanga
hau dat pikin dɛm mek nyanga!
Tek smɔl rop bigin fɔ tai
wan wan pis fɔ ɛni sai;
45   dɛn dɛm put di krɔs fɔ grɔng
fɔ Mami Bɔl i fain kampɔng.
Wan taim kɔk bigin fɔ kɔl
kukaruku fɔ dɛm ɔl.
Pit, pit, pit! dɛm hɔri tri
50   fain di chɔp dɛm no fit si.
kɔk an hɛn dɛm chɔp wan pat
dɛn dɛm fia fɔ dɛm hat!
No bɛt nau no fit fɔ go
seka rop di holam so.
55   Dɛm pul, dɛm pul fɔ muf dat chɔp,
dɛm rɔn dis sai, dɛm flai fɔ ɔp.
Wandaful! Yu sɛf fit si
bɛt dɛm hang fɔ dis bik tri.
Nɛk dɔng lɔng, dɛm ai dɔng dak
60   ɛni faul di fia pas mak.
Hɛn dɛm hala, klos dɛm ai,
lei las ek sɛf, dɛn dɛm dai.
Mami Bɔl i wɔk fɔ pala
hia di krai, di lɔng wehala;
65   sabi fain sɔm ting wowo,
lɛf i hɔs, fɔ baksai go.
Wei! di ting wei mit i ai!
Ashia Mami! Krai, krai, krai.
"Ɔl di ting wei bin di swit mi
70   hau dis bad lɔk so bin mit mi?
Ɔl ting wei a laik fɔ si
luk, dɛm hang nau so fɔ tri."
Mami wei i sɔri pas
kɔt dɛm rop wit i kɔtlas.
75   Sɔri dei so fɔ i ai
as i shua di bɛt dɔng dai.
Sɔfri, sɔfri go fɔ hɔs
wit di bɛt wei i dɔng lɔs.
Dis na kɔni nɔmba wan –
80   Wet nau fɔ sɔm ɔda wan.

NƆMBA TU KƆNI

Mami Bɔl bin hol kraidai
dɛn i stɔp, i tɔs i ai,
mɛmba sei i gud fɔ chɔp
di bɛt so smɔl i dai fɔ ɔp.
85   Tink sei i go kukam hɔt,
rostam fain fɔ sɔm big pɔt.

Max na Moritz, tupela manki,
i laik kirapim pasin kranki.
Tupela i kisim bret,
40   katim na pasim em long tret,
long hap i kam, long hap i go,
tu go kros long tupela mo,
olsem kampas poin i stap.
Putim nau, tupela i lap,
45   putim i stap long gutpela graun
na wet long kakaruk i kam daun.
Ol i kamap nau na luk,
dispela fopela kakaruk;
man i singaut: Kokoriku!
50   na kuk-kuk-kuk, ol meri tu.
Fopela i daunim bret
wanpela wanpela, wantaim tret.
Na taim i laik i go bek gen,
o sori brata! i no ken.
55   Fopela i pas long rop long nek –
no ken gohet, no ken bek.
Ol i raun na longlong tru –
tarangu, o tarangu!
Ol i kam hangamap long huk
60   bilong diwai, fopela kakaruk,
na rop i skruim nek i go
na ol i no ken singaut mo.
Tripela meri i dropim kiau
na dai i kisim fopela nau.
65   Na lapun meri i stap insait,
i harim nois na kam ausait.
Em i lukim samting nogut
i bin kamap long kakaruk.
Em i lukim, em i krai,
70   wara i kamap long ai.
"O sori, kas anlaki tru!
Mi lus, mi blu, o tarangu!"
Belhevi nau, em i go kisim
samting bilong lusim fopela pisin
75   Long busnaip nau i katim daun,
fopela i pundaun long graun.
Em i krai, singaut long maus,
holim na go bek long haus.
Dispela trik i nambawan tru;
80   bai yu harim namba tu.

TRIK NAMBA TU

Na dispela Bolte, lapun meri,
longtaim nau i pilim hevi
long kakaruk em i bin lusim,
na tingting nau long we bilong yusim.
85   Em i ting olsem: 'Mobeta –
olsem nogut mi wet, a? –

Dis fi look pan dem puor ting
wha did walk about an sing,
niekid now pan kitchen tieble
90   kot ar suol muor dan she ieble.
She memba ow a maanin time
dem ron meet ar, bright an prime,
scratchin worm all roun de yaad
while de roosta keep de gaad.
95   Ar lickle daag an she feel bad.
H'outside Max an Marris glad:
"Quick! De roof!" an op dem climb,
look dong de chimbley in time
fi see chicken-dem a ruos,
100   season good, an brown like tuos.
Laad! De sight sweet dem kyaan don
fi watch de fowl jomp an ton
wid de skellion in de dutch-pat
pan de faya blazin hat.
105   Mada Bolt usual fi eat
pickle tings wid fresh ruos meat,
so she tek wan plate an gaan
dong de cella weh she paan
de pickle-backle. She no see
110   de ouse-tap ave h'activity.
Max lang-ead tell im fi bring
fish-hook fasten well pan string:
Yai! De fos chicken a com!
Nomba two hincrease de sum.
115   A wha dis? See Nomba Tree
fly op quicka dan a flea!
Nomba Fuor com op at laas,
bot Poppop see all wha pass
an baak afta de two sinna
120   weh tief out de lady dinna.
Mada Bolt siem time com een
see de dutch-pat empty clean!
Like when Lot wife ton eena saal,
Mada Bolt kyaan move at all.
125   Troble now! De daag a growl
bot dem jomp gaan wid de fowl.
"Bad Poppop!" she dis bawl out,
"A mus fi-yuh greedy mout!
Dis time me gwine pay you aaf,
130   beat yuh prapa tell yuh saaf!"
She tek wan iron spoon so big
it could use fi feedin pig,
lick de daag wid all ar strent:
Puor im know im innocent.
135   Mean time Max an Marris feas
clean don leavin suo-so piece.
In de bush dem sleepin soun
stretch out snuorin pan de groun.
Dis-ya badness mek de secan –
140   quick time falla a nex wan.

(afta i dɔn ros dɛm gud)
kwayɛt fashin fɔ im fud.
Bɔt, fɔ tɔk tru, i sɔri
90   we i si dɛm po bɔdi
na di faya nekɛd wan,
dɛm we kin de krach sansan
na yad ɛn gadin ɔl tɛm
(dat na bifo dis mit dɛm).
95   Mami Bolt bigin fɔ kray,
im dɔg Spits timap wan say.
Maks ɛn Mɔris kech di sɛnt:
"di ruf, kwik, dis luk ɔjɛnt!"
Frɔm di chimni dɛm gladi,
100   di chikin dɛm gud fɔ si,
dɛm ed ɛn nɛk dɔn kɔmɔt
ɛn luk dɛm de fray na pɔt.
Mami Bolt de kam dɔng ya
kwik na im ɔnda sɛla.
105   i ɔl ayɛn spun na an
fɔ pul shakpa, lili wan;
na sup we i lɛk fɔ it
ɛn na we i wam i swit.
Na di chimni ɔp di ruf
110   dɛm si se dɛm kech awuf.
Maks bin dɔn mek ɔl im plan,
uk ɛn fishin-rɔd na an.
Es am ɔp! gud ɛn prɔpa,
fɔs chikin fɔ im sɔpa.
115   Es am ɔp! nɔmba tu go,
na nɔmba tri de kam so,
naw di las wan nɔmba fo:
izi, man, na dɛm dɔn so! –
Ɔldo Spits si wetin bi
120   ɛn bak "baw waw" we i si,
di bɔbɔ dɛm wit di fɔl
nɔ timap wes tɛm atɔl.
Dis min ɔda wahala
We Mami Bolt kam bak, a!
125   Di sayt we im tu yay si
na im fray pan, po Mami!
Chikin gon! I nɔ si wan!
Ɛn na Spits i fɔdɔm pan.
"O Spits, yu wikɛd dɛbul,
130   na yu a gɛt fɔ andul!"
Big, ebi ayɛn spun, o
na im i es pan Spits so.
Spits ala lawd, i at am
bikɔs nɔto im du am.
135   Maks ɛn Mɔris de de snɔ
bɛlful wan, dɛm nɔ want mɔ.
Ɛn pan ɔl di chikin sɛf
na wan lɛg nɔmɔ naw lɛf.
Na di sɛkɛn bad trik dis.
140   Luk di tɔd, lɛ yu nɔ mis.

Bɔt i sɔri so na dai
wɛn i luk di bɛt fɔ ai.
Ɔl dɛm feda nau dɔng go
90 lɛf di bɛt dɛm neked so.
Di bɛt wei bin di soso plei
krach di grɔng so ɛni dei,
nau fɔ gadɛn, nau fɔ bak,
soso muf muf, nɛva slak.
95 Wei! Mami Bol bigin fɔ krai,
Masa Dɔg dei fɔ i sai.
Tar an Tava hia di smɛl,
tɔk sei mek wi klaim ɔp wɛl.
So dɛm klaim fɔ ɔp mbanda
100 luk fɔ dɔng, bigin fɔ wanda.
Langa mek dɛm mɔt dɛm wɛt
as dɛm luk di foa bɛt.
Jɔsnau, Mami go fɔ ɔt
gɛt sɔm ɔda chɔp fɔ pɔt,
105 fain sɔm njamanjama tu,
no bi plenti, smɔl go du.
Mami laik dis chɔp pas ɔl
bɔt i gɛt fɔ hɔtam smɔl.
Stil, fɔ ruf di boi dɛm dei,
110 mek kɔni fɔ i sotei.
Tar, lɔng hed, i no fɔgɛt
tek i stik fɔ fish ɔ bɛt.
So i muf i lɔng lɔng stik
huk di fɔs hɛn ɔp kwik kwik;
115 nɔmba tu i huk agɛn
dɛn i tot anɔda hɛn.
Las taim nau di pikin wɔk,
tek i stik, wikɔp di kɔk.
Wandaz! "Wi dɔng winam ɔl."
120 Masa Dɔg bigin fɔ kɔl,
kɔl sei "Ak!" fɔ Mami so,
bɔt di boi dɛm bin rɔn go.
Hɔt go kam fɔ Masa Ak –
Mami Bol di ritɔn bak.
125 Ɔl i faul bin waka go
Mama Bol bin vɛks daso.
Mami stan laik stɔn fɔ lan
wɛn i si di ɛmti pan.
"Ɔl di faul wei lɔs fɔ dei,
130 Masa Dɔg, na yu go pei."
Wit i mɔta stik krik krak
wam! fɔ Masa Dɔg i bak.
Dɔg i muf sɔm krai fɔ ɔp –
i sabi sei i nɛva chɔp.
135 Tar an Tava dɔng chɔp ova,
nau dɛm slip fɔ ɔnda kɔva.
Daso wan smɔl fut rimɛn
fɔ di kɔk an di tri hɛn.
Dis na kɔni nɔmba tu –
140 luk di nɛks bad ting dɛm du.

mobeta mi kukim ol na kaikai;
mi ken kaikai wantaim krai.'
Na krai bilongen i strong, ating,
90 taim i lukim i stap skin nating
long tebol, redi nau long kuk,
dispela fopela kakaruk,
fopela i bin save pilai
na raun long gaten na haus olde.
95 Meri i bin stat long hevi gen
na dok i hevi wantaim em.
Max na Moritz i harim smel
bilong kuk – swit moa long bel!
Tupela i kirap, pasim maus,
100 klaim i go antap long haus,
lukim kakaruk i stap daunbilo,
long praipan ol i kuk i go.
Na Meri Bolte i no stap;
em i go long narapela hap.
105 Em i laik i miksim mit
wantaim sampela samting swit:
bin, na kon, na rais, na kabis –
gutpela kaikai, i no rabis!
Long dispela taim long haus antap
110 tupela manki wok i stap
Max i bin ting gut paslain
na i bin kisim i kam pislain.
Haisimap! Em i huk
na kisim wanpela kakaruk.
115 Haisimap! Nau sekan wan.
Haisimap! Namba tri i kam.
Nau i hukim namba foa;
Haisimap! Nau nogat moa.
Dok tasol i lukim nau
120 na i singaut: kabau, kabau!
Tupela i ron hariap
lusim haus na dok i stap.
Na yu ting wonem meri i lukim
taim i laik kam bek na kukim?
125 Ol kakaruk i no stap moa!
Meri sanap pas long plua.
Em i tingting stret long dok.
'Spitz!' i kolim nem i tok.
'O yu bladi rabis samting,
130 mi mekim save yu, ating!'
Em i kisim bikpela spun,
paitim dok long skin na bun.
Dok tasol i singaut strong
bikos i save i no gat rong.
135 Max na Moritz, bel i tait,
slip long wanpela ples i hait.
Long kaikai manki i no slek,
i pinisim inap long tupela lek.
Em i pinis bilong namba tu,
140 nau namba tri mi tokim yu.

BADNESS NOMBA TREE   TƆD TRIK

People in de districk say   Ɔl man na di vilej no
Bock de bes man roun dat way.   Bil, we na man we kin so.
Drodgin clothes ar Sonday bes,   Wɔk klos, trɔsis, Sɔnde kot,
jacket, pants, ar ole-time ves,   dina-kot ɛn ova-kot,
145 tree-piece suit ar winta-coat,   145 wes-kot sɛf wit pɔkit ɔl,
saila-suit fi wear pan boat,   lɛda ban, ɔl tin yu kɔl,
Bock wok good pan all a dis: dɛm ɔl Masta Bil kin so.
Fi-im finga neva miss.   Chɛr klos sɛf we fɔ so, o,
Anyting wha need fi patch,   klos fɔ kɔt ɛn klos fɔ pis,
150 piecen, daan so i wi match.   150 bɔtin fɔ so na trɔsis—
(Ef yuh need anedda botton   aw, usay ɛn wesmata,
Bock wi fix yuh op fi notten).   biɛn, bifo, nɔ mata—
Tielarin of any kine,   ɔl dis Masta Bil go du,
inside, h'outside, ar behine—   na dis i lɛk du, fɔ tru,
155 dat Mass Bock kyan do fi true   155 pas ɔl tin dɔn na dis wɔl.
cause im stody ole an new.   Dat mek, na di tɔng, dɛm ɔl
Dat mek Bock ave good-good niem: lɛk am bad ɛn mek am frɛn
Everybady seh de siem.   pas Maks ɛn Mɔris we bɛn
Dem ginnal try ef dem kyan   fɔ ambɔgin am nɔmɔ—
160 troble dis good destant man.   160 ɛn dɛm tink gud fɔ mek shɔ.
Now, right nex de tiela duor   Unu fɔ no se, bifo
ron de ribba wid a ruor.   Bil in os riva de flo.
Weh de road-way a fi pass   Pantap, wan smɔl brij bin de
bridge buil uova, right acraas.   fɔ krɔs go di ɔda we.
165 Max an Marris sight i good,   165 Maks ɛn Mɔris wikɛd ya!
get wan saw fi kot de wood: Dɛm so bod rika raka,
Creechy-crawchy! Creechy-craw!   Kɔmɔt na di brij kwik wan
kot i paat-way wid de saw.   jɔs fɔ ambɔg di po man.
Loud-loud dem set demself fi bawl   Wɛn dɛm dɔn du dis bad wok,
170 laughin kya-kya when dem call: 170 dɛm bigin ala ɛn jok:
"Cho, com out, man! Show we 'Bock'!   "Kam na do! Dadi Bɔskot!
Tiela een deh? Mock-mock-mock!"   Tela, tela, Bili-Got!"
Bock no easy man fi vex;   Bil kin bia ɔl kayn tin,
tek juok betta dan de nex,   pas fityay frɔm smɔl pikin.
175 bot when dem call im out fi 'bock', 175 So, wɛn i yɛri dis kɔs,
like ram-goat fasten eena mock,   i vɛks sote i wan bɔs.
im vex nuh bad-ants an im paan   I fɛn wan tik ɛn kɔmɔt
de yaad-stick in im han an gaan!   rɔn kam timap na domɔt.
Hear dem: "Mock-mock!" een dem nose,   Egen i yɛri dɛm vɔys
180 an tek op plenty fonny pose.   180 de kɔs am ɛn de mek nɔys.
Him liff-op an mek wan jomp   As i de krɔs di brij brok
an lick de bridge weh go dong "CROMP!"   ɛn na pis pis, nɔto jok.
Head-fos im go dong, puor Bock,   Bak dɛm ala "mɛk, mɛk, mɛk!"
while dem laugh an bawl "Mock-mock!"   ɛn, plɔp! Tela Bil dɔn rɛk!
185 *Dem* liff op an gaan like breeze: 185 As dis apin, tu dɔks swim
Bock a ribba kaaf an sneeze.   kam pas, ɛn skyad wan na im
Two goose com swim down de way;   Tela Bil grip dɛm fut fas,
Bock 'tretch out im han fi pray,   ɛn fɛt te di denja pas.
paan dem foot in aida han,   Mi kin tɛl yu se fɔ tru
190 fly back sief-sief to dry lan.   190 dis na tranga tin fɔ du.

Nɔmba Tri Kɔni

Ɛni man fɔ kɔntri no
telɔ wei i nem Kojo.
Papa Kojo sabi bos
sei i fit mek ɔl kain klos.
145 Trɔsa witi pɛnsɛl fut,
gaun wit pɔkɛt, Sɔndei sut,
danshiki wit trɔsa tu,
abada i sabi du,
lapa dɛm an buba fain –
150 Papa sabi mek ɔlkain.
Palava dei, sɔm botɔn lɔs,
tia fɔ drɛs, ɔ trɔsa bɔs,
Papa sabi fiksam fain,
baksai, lassai, frɔn, bihain –
155 ɔl ting dɛm i sabi so,
na han-wɔk dis fɔ ol Kojo.
Ɛni man fɔ ɛni pat
laik di telɔ fɔ i hat.
Tar an Tava plan sei nɛks
160 tam dɛm mek wi papa vɛks.
Fɔ bifoa wi telɔ doa
riva dei wei tumtum moa.
Smɔl brij dei fɔ wata bak
laik sɔm kɔntri kain hamak.
165 Tar an Tava no di res
tek sɔm sɔ nau fɔ sɔm ples,
tek dɛm sɔ, bigin fɔ kɔt
mindru brij. Kojo hia hɔt.
Wɛn dɛm wɔk i finish ɔl
170 dɛn dɛm stat bigin fɔ kɔl.
"Kɔmɔt jakas, kam Kojo,
yu sabi sei yu fes wowo?
Telɔ man, yu ɔgli bad,
Kojo, Kojo, mad, mad, mad!"
175 Kojo sabi lisɛn wɛl
fɔ di ting wei man fit tɛl,
bɔt i hat bigin fɔ krak
wɛn i hia dat kɔs fɔ bak.
Wantaim wit i mita stik
180 go fɔ doa, muf i kwik,
fɔ i hia dɛm kɔl fɔ yad:
"Kojo, Kojo, mad, mad, mad!"
Dɛn wi telɔ hala ha!
Fɔ di brij wei chakara.
185 Bifoa i hia anɔda kɔl
Masa Telɔ dɔng go ɔl.
Bɔt wi papa gɛt gud lɔk
fɔ i si sɔm tu fain dɔk,
wei di swim fɔ wata shut!
190 Masa grab dɛm fɔ dɛm fut.

Trik Namba Tri

I no gat wanpela man long ples
i no save gut long pes
bilong dispela man ol i kolim Bok.
Ologeta de i save wok
145 samapim klos – trausis, sket,
singlis, blaus, blujins, let;
bisnis bilongen i bin kirapim
long wokim klos na samapim.
O sapos sok bilong yu i gat hul,
150 i save pasim hul long wul.
O baten bilong yu i lus,
pundaun na i lus long bus,
nogat wari, nogat tok:
karim ol samting i go long Bok,
155 em i stretim long gutpela pasin,
fiksim ol klos long masin.
Ol pipel, man, meri, dok,
i save laikim dispela Bok.
Max na Moritz i makim kos
160 bilong mekim dispela man i kros.
Nau yu mas save, wanpela baret
i ron i go long haus long poret.
Na wanpela bris yu ken lukim,
na rot i go long wara i brukim.
165 Max na Moritz i kamap hait,
ating long apinun o nait;
long so i singaut: rasiris!
tupela katim plang long bris.
I pinis nau, tupela i was
170 long haus bilong Bok na tok bilas.
'He, yu kamaut, blakbokis Bok,
blakbokis, blakbokis, Bok, Bok, Bok!'
Bok i man i no save sem
long harim ologeta nem
175 tasol nem 'blakbokis' em i hetim
na tupela manki i laik stretim.
Em i ron i kam ausait,
holim stik na em i laik pait,
olosem tupela yet i tok:
180 'blakbokis, blakbokis, Bok, Bok, Bok!'
I kros tru olsem man i spak;
i ron long bris – na plang i krak!
Tupela i singaut: 'blakbokis, Bok!'
na Bok i stap nau wantaim prok.
185 Bok em i no save swim,
wara i laik daunim em.
Klosap i dai – o pekato!
Tasol i lukim tupela pato,
holim tupela strong long lek
190 long sua nau em i kam bek.

Wha maanin spwile, night kyaan cure.
Bock feel im belly very suor.
Kuol-waata fram de ribba gripe im
like mango eena son-hat ripin.
195 Notten frighten Mass Bock wife:
She boun fi save ar husban life.
She tek hat-iron draw de kuol
out im belly, good as guol!
News flash troo de neighbahood:
200 "Bock betta! Bock feelin good!"
Dis mek badness Nomba Tree –
nex wan comin quick yuh see!

Badness Nomba Fuor

Ole-time people mek wan rule:
"Learn and study while in school!"
205 ABC kyan ongle staat
lov a knallidge in de haat:
Readin, writin, ritmetick
kyan gi Sietan wan good lick,
higle smaddy wid no fait
210 fine demself a Debbil gate;
show respeck an lov de wise:
Solomon wi gi yuh prize!
Stody ow fi ondastan
all de ways a Gad an man.
215 In all learnin, Teacha Lampel
set de very bes example;
siek a dat, Marris an Max
scaan im woss dan chicken-pax.
Lampel lov fi smuok wan pipe.
220 Jackass-caan een deh, well ripe.
School gi worries widout cease,
teacha need som res an peace
fram de nize an badaration
a de yonga generation.
225 Max an Marris stody plan
fi mek worries fi de man:
Sence tobacco uova-sweet im
jackass-caan an pipe wi beat im.
Puor ole teacha soffarin
230 mek de bway-dem laugh like sin.
Sonday maanin church-bell ring
time fi com com pray an sing;
at de aagan Teacha playin
while im haat in quiet prayin.
235 In im affice tief de bway
out fi rab an fi destray:
Max tek Teacha pipe in han
– bes pipe mek in any lan –
while dat wotliss Marris self
240 tek gonpowda aaf de shelf.

Wetin bi bikɔs ɔf dat
im bɛlɛ bigin fɔ at.
Misis Bil na im go fɛn
wan kayn ɔt ɛn flat ayɛn.
195 Wi fɔ prez di ledi o,
na im mek i nɔ day go.
Na im kol bɛlɛ i wam
we mek im wɛl bɔdi kam.
ɛn sun, as yu sɛf kin tɛl,
200 ɔl man de se "Bil dɔn wɛl."
Na di tɔd bad trik dis mayn.
Nɔmba fo bigin nɛks layn.

Nɔmba fo

Dɛm kin se, ɛn misɛf gri,
man fɔ lan pas' ABC.
205 Wetin go pliz God insɛf
na if wi bɛtɛ wisɛf.
Rayt ɛn rid nɔto ɔl o,
pɔsin we gɛt sɛns fɔ no.
Nɔto arifmitik wan
210 pɔsin fɔ tray gud wan pan;
i fɔ gladi fɔ lisin
we big wan de gi lɛsin.
Ticha Lampel ɔlwez si
dat i du dis wit sabi.
215 Bɔt dɛm wi bad bad bɔbɔ
nɔ bin lɛk am fɔ dis, nɔ.
U dɔn yus fɔ bi raskɛl
tink ticha kin go to ɛl.
Dis gud ticha bin lɛk smok,
220 ɛn wɛn man dɔn kɔmɔt wok,
afta i dɔn yagba dɔn,
gud ol man kin smok fɔ fɔn.
A nɔ tink ɛnibɔdi
go se i nɔ gri wit mi.
225 Maks ɛn Mɔris bisin de?
Fɔ dɛm, na raskɛl de pe.
Dɛm sidɔm dɛm bren de wok –
"aw dis pɛp we i de smok?"
Wɛn dis gud man wan Sɔnde
230 ɔnɛs wan sidɔm de ple
ɔgan na di chɔch fayn wan,
as na bin gud gud chɔch man,
di bɔbɔ dɛm jɛs tipto
na ɔp im os dɛm go so.
235 As dɛm rich dɛm fɛn im pɛp;
Maks ol am na an de ɛp,
Mɔris pul gɔn pawda, nit,
we bin de na im pɔkit.
I tɔn am te di pɛp ful
240 ɛn, kwik, dɛm go om saful.

Telɔ sabi fia na dai,
bɔt di dɔk fɔ drai grɔng flai.
Masa dei jɔsnau fɔ grɔng
an i bele di hɔt trɔng.
195 Mama Kojo tek i man,
ɔl ting dei nau fɔ i han.
Wit sɔm aiɔn rɛt laik gol
fɔ i bele drɔ di kol.
Smɔl taim fɔ ɔl kɔna dɛn:
200 "Masa Kojo wɛl agɛn."
Dis na kɔni nɔmba tri –
ɔda wan wi gɛt fɔ si.

Nɔmba Foa Kɔni

Panapu dei, a raitam dɔng:
"Man mɔs lɛn fɔ dis wi grɔng."
205 No bi daso A, B, C,
mek wi sabi hau fɔ bi.
No bi ɔl sɛns dei fɔ tali
Chinda sabi dis fɔ Bali.
Man i gɛt fɔ lisɛn wɛl
210 fɔ di tru wi papa tɛl.
Pa Matyu, wi katakis,
sabi ɔl gut fashɔn dis,
an i glad fɔ tich wi tru
ɔl di ting man gɛt fɔ du.
215 Tar an Tava, sɔf laik san,
no fit laik dis Gɔd i man.
Ɛni boi wei di bɛnbɛn
No di hia dɛm ticha dɛn.
Pa Matyu, a no tɔk lai,
220 sabi smok tabak na dai.
No man no fit blem i sei
i no gɛt rait fɔ ɔl kain plei.
Afta wɔk fɔ tekwe sin
i gut i fit ɛnjoi i skin.
225 Tar an Tava tink i fɔni
nak dis ol man wit dɛm kɔni.
Dɛm sabi sei i laik fɔ smok
fɔ i paip dɛm plan sɔm jok.
Sɔndei kam an ol Pa Mat
230 go fɔ chɔs, i muf i hat,
plei gegeru sɔfli so,
sing di mek di savis go.
Wɛn i dei fɔ Gɔd i chɔs
pikin dɛm go fɔ i hɔs.
235 Tar tink sei di paip fɔ stan;
luk, i tekam fɔ i han.
Tava tek gɔn pɔda ɔt,
putam fɔ di paip i mɔt.
Dɛm wan hɔri fɔ di hɔs,
240 Hawe pipul lɛf di chɔs.

Tasol ol samting i no stret;
Bok i no drai, skin i wet,
na em i kisim sik long bel;
skin i pen, na het, na tel!
195 Tasol Bok i gat gutpela meri;
em i no slek, em i no wari,
em i gat save narakain –
em i go kisim ain!
Em i ainimaut ol pen
200 na Bok i pilim orait gen!
Pinis nau nambatri trik,
namba foa i kamap kwik.

Trik Namba Foa

Long ol ples i gat rul
ol manmeri i mas skul.
205 Rit na rait na ABC
i save mekim man i fri.
Man i no gat save long ol namba
i gat het olosem kukamba.
Man i no save wok bilong gavman
210 em i no man tru, tasol i hapman.
Ologeta samting bilong skul
man i no save, em i ful.
Na bilong givim gutpela eksampel
mi tok long wanpela tisa, Lempel.
215 Max na Moritz tasol i les
long laikim tisa long dispela ples;
ol lesbaga i no ken yesa
long ol samting bilong tisa.
Na dispela tisa i smokim paip,
220 em i laikim olsem laip.
De na nait em i no lus
long painim taim bilong pulim brus.
Pasin bilongen; i no sin
sapos man i smok bilong kisim win.
225 Max na Moritz kru i skrapim
bilong painim we bilong bagarapim
dispela tisa; tupela i laik
long painim we bilong stilim paip.
Tupela i wet na tingting planti,
230 inap long wanpela de long Sande
em i bin go long misa
na pilai long ogan, dispela tisa.
Tupela manki i wokabaut hait
i go long haus, i go insait,
235 painim paip long haus i stap.
Max i holim, tupela i lap.
Moritz i kisim paura bilong gan,
holim strong long tupela han;
ol strongpela paura bilong pairap
240 i go long paip i pulimap.

Quick dem 'crape de powda out,
full de pipe fram stem to spout,
tip-toe swif an gaan dem ways
while a church de laas hymn raise.

245 Nex ting Teacha tek de keys,
lack op good an seek im ease
afta all im duty don,
quiet canscience lead im on.
Reachin ome, im siddong where
250 pipe an matches by de chair;
den im strike de match an say:
"Peace on earth is all I pray!"
BRADDAM! BANGARANG! Pipe bus!
Pencil, blatta, ton to dus!
255 Tieble, chair an des fly weh
mash an crash to pure pre-pre!
Smuok clear op widout a soun,
teacha flat dong pan de groun.
Praises be, im no dead yet,
260 but im fies ton black as jet.
Black de nose, eye-brow an han
blacka dan ole pudden-pan.
Head now clean nuh cricket-ball!
Hair singe gaan, non leave at all!
265 Who gwine teach, explain an show
pickney ow true knallidge grow?
Den fi service, who gwine play
ef Mass Lampel stay away?
Pipe im lov, an dat nuh mash
270 disappear like suo-so trash?
Sickness betta when time due,
bot when pipe mash, i mash fi true.
Dis mek Badness Nomba Fuor –
Nomba Five wi show yuh muor.
275 Ef yuh ave wan h'oncle weh
live a tong or contry, seh,

Badness Nomba Five

treat im prapa, good an kine,
neva mek im feel bad-mine.
Call out: "Nice good maanin, wha
280 yuh waan me bring yuh, sah?"
Gwaan get anything im wish:
pipe, newspiepa, tea, fry fish.
Rob im dong fi back-pain, suor,
whatsoever yuh kyan cure:
285 was'-sting, h'ants-bite, belly-ache,
bring bush tea fi uncle sake.
When im draw im pipe too aad,
Chuokin, sneezin roun de yaad,
prapa nephew ron com quick:
290 "Tek time h'oncle! No get sick!"

If yu si we dɛm de rɔn
as chɔch savis sun go dɔn.
Na di chɔch savis dɔn so,
Lampɛl jɛs de lɔk chɔch-do,
245 saful wan; i bin dɔn pik
im im buk ɛn im myuzik.
Na im os i de go so
de tɛnk Gɔd as i de go.
I layt im pɛp, dis gud pa,
250 ɛn de se to insɛf "A,
natin na dis wɔl nɔ fayn
lɛk fɔ gɛt satisfay maynd."
"Bum", na di pɛp faya so
big big ɛn lawd lawd wan o.
255 Wata-glas ɛn kɔfi-pɔt,
tabaka-bɔks ɛn ink-pɔt,
stov, tebul ɛn izi chia
ɔl flay we di pɛp faya.
Wɛn di smok pas wi si se
260 Lampɛl (Gɔd tɛnki!) stil de;
bɔt na im bak i ledɔn
wit sɔm smɔl brus, na di grɔn.
Nos ɛn an ɛn fes ɛn yes
blak lɛkɛ blak man kayn fes,
265 ɛn di las las ia sɛf
na im ed bɔn, nɔn nɔ lɛf.
Udat go tich dɛm pikin
ɛn mek dɛm gɛt buk lanin?
Udat go du ɔl tin, tu,
270 we Lampɛl bin yus fɔ du?
Wetin di ticha fɔ smok
we im pɛp dɔn pwɛl ɛn brok?
Wi go si as tɛm de rɔn;
bɔt di pɛp im yon dɔn dɔn.
275 Dis na di nɔmba fo trik
ɛn nɔmba fayv apin kwik.

Nɔmba Fayv

Vilej ɔ tɔng pɔsin we
gɛt in ɔnkul wit am de
fɔ sho rɛspɛkt ɛn trenin
280 mek i si am lɛk pɔsin.
Se: "Gud mɔnin!" we do klin:
"Ɔnkul, yu want ɛnitin?"
Bring im pɛp ɛn im layta
ɛn di mɔnin nyuzpepa.
285 If tin chuk ɔ bɛt di pa
ɔ krach im bak, nɔ go fa,
na yu ɔnkul, yu fɔ lɛk
fɔ atɛnd am bifo jɛk.
If afta i it im snɔf
290 i tɔn fɔ sniz trɔng ɛn nɔf,

Pa Matyu i klos chɔs doa,
glad pas hau i bin bifoa;
wit i preya buk fɔ han
go fɔ hɔs dis holi man.

245 Gladi mek i hat fit bɔs,
tek i paip wit faia tɔs:
"Gratia tu Tata fain,
He gives peace for all mankain."
Bum! di paip krai laik sɔm gɔn

250 wei dɛm shut. Dis na dɛm fɔn.
Ɔl ting chakara fɔ 'bum':
Pɔt an bol wei dei fɔ rum,
tebul, stov, wan lam, wan chia
ɔl di flai, yu no di hia?

255 Wɛn di smok bin waka go
man fit si wi papa so,
lai fɔ grɔng fɔ mindru hɔs
laik sɔm bebi-dɔl wei lɔs.
Han an fes an fut ɔl blak

260 i lai laik ninga fɔ i bak,
an i hɛd drai laik futbɔl –
Faia holam bɔnam ɔl.
Hu nau fit fɔ tich pikin,
lɛn dɛm gut rot, sho dɛm sin,

265 lɛn dɛm hau fɔ het tonton
Hau fɔ fɔlɔ gut fashɔn?
Hu go chɔp Pa Mat i chia?
Hu di katkis gaun fit wia?
Wɛti Pa go du fɔ smok

270 wei i paip i ɔl dɔng brok?
Taim kul hat fɔ ɔl kain ting,
bɔt dat paip wei fit fɔ king
man fɔ fiksam dei? No, no,
ɔl i swit, i paua go.

275 Dis na kɔni nɔmba foa –
wet nau, wuna go si moa.

Nɔmba Faiv Kɔni

Man fɔ kɔntri ɔ fɔ tɔng
wei gɛt i pa an i shidɔng
fɔ i kɔna gɛt fɔ sho

280 gut fashɔn nau fɔ i no
Pa go laikam taim no dei
i go gɛt i on gut pei.
Fɔ mɔningtam yu gɛt fɔ tɔk:
"Mɔning o! Ashia fɔ wɔk!

285 Yu wan samting, tɔk nau tru
tɛl mi wɛti a fit du."
Jɔs go nau, mek i no taia,
fainam pepa, paip ɔ faia;
ɔ if sɔm mɔskito bait

290 fiks i skin fɔ dei ɔ nait.

Nau tupela i go long rot tu,
olsem i harim pinis bilong lotu.
Lotu i pinis, Lempel i hepi
olsem wanpela liklik bebi.

245 Buk na pepa em i kisim,
sampela wok i laik i pinisim.
Tasol pastaim i laik smok
bipo long kirapim dispela wok.
Olsem long taim bilong rait

250 i gutpela, sapos paip i lait.
'A!' i tok, 'smok i go
i gutpela long malolo!'
Kabum! paip i singaut
long paura, pairap nabaut!

255 Ol tikap, spun, na glas, na naip,
ol i pairap wantaim paip!
Tebol tu, na pen, na ing,
ol i pairap tu, ating.
Nau klaut bilong paura i dai;

260 lukim Lempel – maiomai!
Long plua long baksait i slip
na ol samting i stap long hip.
Skin i blak olsem Buka,
het i kela olsem kuka.

265 Paura i bin kukim em –
long piksa yu ken lukim em.
Husat nau bai i skulim manki
long lusim ologeta pasin kranki?
Husat bai i bosim standet ten

270 sapos Lempel em i no ken?
Na bai i mekim wonem spak
sapos i no ken smok tabak?
Ating bai i kamap orait.
Paip tasol i no ken lait.

275 Pinis long trik namba foa,
tanim pes na ritim moa.

Trik Namba Faiv

Man i stap long ples, o raun
long maket, o sindaun long taun,
em i mas ting long famili,

280 na em i mas ting long kandere.
Kandere i wanlain bilongen,
na em i mas tok gut longen,
givim kambang, buai, daka –
em i gutpela pasin, laka?

285 Sapos natnat i kaikaim em,
yu mas lukaut na paitim em.
Sapos kandere i gat kus,
yu ken waipim kus long nus
long hankisip; o em i sik,

290 yu mas lukautim tu-tri wik.

When im reach ome late a night
tek im boot aaf quick an bright;
bring im slippers, nightshirt, ves,
waam an clean so im kyan res.
295 Fine out wha gi oncle ease
try yuh bes fi mek im please.
Was'e a time me tell yuh seh
Max an Marris no een deh.
H'Oncle Joe gwine soffa bad –
300 Hear dem plan fi mek im mad.
Maybog time com roun again
noff maskitta, plenty rain,
flyin inseck everywhere
singin, buzzin in de air.
305 Max an Marris shake wan tree
maybog drap out like daag-flea.
Swif dem grab dem, bag dem op,
bag like sinting buy fram shap,
pack dem dong de bedfoot tight
310 set fi oncle in de night.
H'oncle Joe de night gaan bed,
– peaceful 'eart an quiet 'ead –
'tretch im bady now fi sleep
like good Christian, lang an deep.
315 Wips-waps! Maachin pan de sheet
maybog tek de bed fi street;
right op Oncle Joe nose-hole
see de leada gaan fi stroll!
"Lawks! A wha dis?" h'oncle paan
320 maybog lang-foot: bedtime gaan!
Koo im jomp op out de bed,
dash weh blanket, sheet, bedspread!
"Lawd!" Im bax wan fram im neck,
nex wan aaf im foot im tek,
325 dem a crawl an climb an fly
pan im han, im clothes, im yeye.
Temparated now kyaan dong
h'oncle mash dem pan de grong.
Lawd be praise! De badaration
330 don wid maybog murderation.
Oncle shet im yeye so sleep:
Koo im snuorin saaf an deep.
Nomba Five a dis-ya trick –
Nomba Six wi falla quick.
335 Easta haliday a fun:
Bieka biek big Easta bun,

BADNESS NOMBA SIX

ginja-bread an bullah kiek –
hongry belly boun fi ache.
Max an Marris mout well set:
340 biscuit, bullah – dem mus get!

yu fɔ se to am fɔ tru
"Gɔd blɛs yu – gud ɛlth to yu."
ɔ if sɛf i kam om let
yu fɔ pul im sus, nɔ wet
295 ɛn bring slipas as i drap
ɛn im drɛsin-gawn ɛn kyap
mek i nɔ go lɛf na kol –
ɛnitin fɔ pliz im sol.
Maks ɛn Mɔris bisin de?
300 Luk di bad gem we dɛm ple
pan ɔnkul Frits, a po man!
(Unu sabi aw dɛm tan).
Ɔl man sabi gɔngrɔbi
we lɛk fɔ flay na tik fri
305 ɛn fɔ krip; dat nɔ to ɔl,
bikɔs na so dɛm lɛk krɔl.
Maks ɛn Mɔris jɛs kam kwik,
shek di tin dɛm frɔm di tik.
Dɛm bin bring pepa bag kam
310 So dɛm kech plɛnti wit am.
Dɛm kɛr dɛm go ayd dɛm fayn
na Ɔnkul Frits im bed, mayn.
Ɔnkul Frits go ledɔn slip
as di de dɔn dɔn dis trip.
315 I sɛt yay, drɔ oba am
im aydadawn, slip fɔ am.
Bɔt di tin dɛm kɔmɔt kwik,
ɔnda di matrɛs, dɛm snik.
Sɛf dɛm lida jɛs de dos
320 Ɔnkul Frits na im po nos.
"A, wetin dis?" I ala
as i ɔl di ɛlɛya,
ɛn yu kin si am, i fred
de jomp kɔmɔt na im bed.
325 "Awch", ɔda wan bɛt im nɛk,
lɛg ɛn ɔl usay dɛm lɛk.
Dɛm de krip ɛn bɔz ɛn flay
na ya, yanda ɛn ɔl say.
Ɔnkul Frits grap kil dɛm dɔn,
330 i nak ɛn stamp dɛm na grɔn.
Luk dɛm na grɔn, ɔl dɔn day,
yu kyant si wan sɛf nɔ say.
Naw Ɔnkul kin sɛt im yay
ɛn slip te i satisfay.
335 Na trik nɔmba fayv dɔn so.
Luk nɔmba siks aw i go.

NƆMBA SIKS

Ista tɛm we fɔ gladi
wɛn dɛm beka we oli
kin bek ɛn mek plɛnti swit,
340 Maks ɛn Mɔris se dɛm fit

If i put snɔf an i snis
tɔk sei: "Mek Gɔd laik yu, plis."
If i kam bak let fɔ nait,
mek yu si i dei ɔl rait;
295 mek yu muf i shu ɔ but,
put sɔm sandal fɔ i fut,
gɛt i gaun, i kap fɔ hɛd,
wɔm i fain, dɛn drɛs i bɛd.
Tar an Tava no fit si
300 hau dis kain wɔk gɛt fɔ bi.
Mek wi luk hau dɛm bin nak
Pa Mangan wit dɛm hambak.
Ɛni man nau sabi fain
kɔkroch dɛm wei flai an shain,
305 kɔkroch wɛda shɔt ɔ lɔng
dɛm dei laik krɔkrɔ fɔ wi grɔng.
Tar an Tava soso bat
fain di kɔkroch fɔ ɔl pat;
kach dɛm, put dɛm fɔ tu kwa,
310 go mek kɔni fɔ dis Pa.
Dis tu trɔng-ai boi dɛm hɛd
put di bif fɔ Pa i bɛd.
Taim fɔ slip, so fɔ i bɛd
go Pa Mangan, kap fɔ hɛd,
315 lai dɔng sɔf, fɔ matras krip,
klos i ai, bigin fɔ slip.
Pit, pat, pit! dɛm kɔkroch trai
waka rich Pa Mangan ai.
Lidaman trɛchɔt i han
320 tɔs di nos fɔ Pa Mangan.
"Wei hele! Na wich kain tif?"
Papa luk di wowo bif.
Mangan jɔm fɔ di bɛd sai,
fia hol i so na dai.
325 "Ena!" Ɔda wan i nak
fɔ i fut, i nɛk, i bak.
Dɛm rɔn fɔ hia, dɛm flai fɔ ɔp –
Pa Mangan di mash dɛm "Bɔp!"
Laik tri fɔ bris i muf i han,
330 kil dɛm hɔha dis gud man.
Wuna luk nau, fait dɔng dai,
fɔ di grɔng dɛm kɔkroch lai.
Pa Mangan bin kil dɛm ɔl,
bifoa i fit lai dɔng slip smɔl.
335 Kɔni nɔmba faiv dei so –
fɔ nɔmba siks wi tɔn nau go.

Nɔmba Siks Kɔni

Fɔ Ista tam wi skin di glad,
ɔl man trai fɔ lɛf dɛm bad.
Chɔp-haus man pripia i shɔp
340 mek fain ting fɔ wi fɔ chɔp,

Na sapos kandere i spak,
kambek long haus long tudak,
yu mas helpim em, lusim su,
mekim em i go slip tru,
295 karimapim i no kol,
putim blanket, olsem tasol.
Em i pasin bilong ol famili,
pasin bilong lukautim kandere.
Max na Moritz i mekim narakain,
300 tupela no belgut long wanlain,
long ol famili o ol mismis;
i laik tasol trikim kandere Fritz.
Tupela i go kisim binatang
– i no korakum, i no lang –
305 tasol bikpela samting i save flai
i kamap sindaun long ol diwai.
Tupela meknaisim tri i go,
kisim binatang planti mo.
Pasim binatang long pepa bek,
310 skruimapim bek long nek.
Long bet we kandere i save slip
tupela i siutim ananit!
Kandere i putim kep long het
na pajama, na i go long bet.
315 Em i slip na pasim ai,
em i slip olsem man i dai.
Tasol binatang i no save slip long nait,
ol i kirap kamaut long lait.
Ol i wokabaut olsem musmus;
320 namba wan i kamap long nus.
'Oloman!' i tok, 'wonem samting, a?'
na em i holim em long pinga.
Em i kirap, em i sanap,
em i lusim bet hariap.
325 'Au au!' i tok; binatang long nek
na long baksait, na long lek!
Ol i flai na em i raunim,
planti binatang tumas long kaunim!
Em i raunim, ol i flai,
330 em i kilim ol i dai.
Pinis nau! No gat moa
binatang i wokabaut long plua.
Kandere i laik pasim ai gen,
tingting long binatang, i no ken.
335 Em namba faiv; na namba sikis
em i trik yu ridim neks.

Trik Namba Sikis

Ista na Krismas, tupela taim
ol i save pati oltaim.
Em i taim yu go long beka
340 baim biskit, ban, na kek, a?

Bot de Bieka no so fool:
lackin shap a fi-im rule.
Tief wha break in Bieka shap
dong de chimbley haffe drap.

345 BRADDAPS! See dem tomble dong
black nuh jang-crow dress fi tong!
BUM! De flour-barrel ketch
dem two tiefin, craven wretch!
Head to foot dem white nuh chalk,

350 woss dan day-ghos' out fi walk!
Bot de bullah pan de shelf
mek dem laugh inside demself.
PASHAI! Chair brok! Dem gaan clean
in de dough in de turreen!

355 PLOP! Dem plasta white wid dough
jus like statue in a row,
nat a church-yaad h'angel stay
whita dan de bway dat day!
Massa Bieka com an see

360 greedy-gut in misary.
Wan-two-tree! Quick-quick im roll
two bread, cova dem op whole!
Bieka oven ruosin hat:
Right inside im shub de lat.

365 Now dem ready, cris an brown,
sweetes bread wha sell a town!
Gaan fa good! Blow loud abeng!
Bot oo baan fi drown kyaan heng.
Krups-krups-krups! Dem chaw de crus

370 siem like rat, an out dem bus.
"What a ting!" de Bieka seh,
"See ow rascal kyan get weh!"
Nomba Six a dis-ya trick –
Nomba Seven falla quick.

Badness Nomba Seven

375 Time fi don, Max an Marris!
Badness kyaan laas lang like dis.
Why dem kottin uopin wide
bag wha full wid caan inside?
Koo ow Faama Green a hais

380 bag pan shoulda, quick an nice.
Scarce wan 'tep im 'tep go out
caan dis scatta all about.
"'Tap.' Wha dis?" Kuol wid fright
faama seh: "De bag feel light!"

385 YAI! Im look een de caan bax
weh im fine Marris an Max.
WAPS! Im pick de wretch-dem out,
bag dem op, an tie de mout.
Max an Marris no feel good

390 carry go a mill like wood.

fɔ gɛt swit tinks fɔ dɛnsɛf.
Bɔt di beka nɔ bin lɛf
di bekri opin nɔ we,
so if pɔsin wan tif de

345 pas i tray so te i fos
insay chimni na di os.
Krɔnch! di tu bɔbɔ dɛm pas
na di chimni, ɛn dɛm fas.
Na so dɛm blak lɛkɛ bat.

350 Pɔf! dɛm drɔp insay kyas flat –
di say di flawa kin kip;
ɛn wet lɛk chɔk, dɛm go dip.
Bɔt dɛm lɛk wetin dɛm mit
bikɔs dɛm dɔn si biskit.

355 Krak! na di chia brok so.
Plɔp! dɛm fɔdɔm na di do!
Luk dɛm we ɔl dɛm bɔdi
kɔba wit do, dɛm sɔri!
Di beka kam, i nɔ te

360 ɛn si di bɔbɔ dɛm de.
Bifo yu se wan, tu, tri,
na tu lof bred dɛm dɔn bi.
Di ovin stil rɛd ɔt! Rɔf!
I put dɛm bak insay! Rɔf!

365 Naw dɛm brawn ɛn du fɔ it.
Ɔl man tink se dɛm dɔn mit
wit trɔbul we dɛm de bet.
Bɔt usay! – Dɛm nɔ day yet.
Lɛk arata dɛm tek tɛm

370 cham cham wetin kɔba dɛm.
ɛn Masta Beka ala
"O Gɔd, dɛm de go yanda!"
Na di nɔmba siks dɔn so.
Bɔt di las wan de kam o.

Nɔmba Sevin

375 Maks ɛn Mɔris, mayn, kyaful!
Dis tɛm una kɔp go ful.
Wetin fɔ mek dɛm ti ya
kɔt ɔl na di bag dɛm, ba?
Fama Mɛk ɔl bag wit kɔn,

380 bɔt i nɔ no ɛn nɔ tɔn,
we im kɔn bigin fɔ drɔp.
I sɔprayz ɛn dɛn i stɔp
ɛn se "dam it, i de layt!"
A! I gladi fɔ di sayt,

385 Maks ɛn Mɔris ayd na kɔn.
Swup! I dɔn shɔbul dɛm dɔn,
di tu yuslɛs bɔbɔ dɛm,
insay im big bag lɔng tɛm.
Maks ɛn Mɔris de fred so

390 as na mil i kɛr dɛm go.

miyɔndɔ, chichi, akara,
kɔki kɔn wit banana.
Hotɛl man i lɔng-hɛd moa,
sabi fain fɔ lɔk i doa.
345 Man wei wan fɔ tiftif i
mɔs kwis i sɛf fɔ chimini.
"Shuf!" di pikin dɛm ɛnta
blak laik kro bɛt fɔ kenja.
"Buf, buf!" fɔ katɔn dɛm fɔl,
350 flaua fɔ kuk di skata ɔl.
Si hau dat tu mɔnki laf,
wait nau so laik pa i baf.
Tar an Tava, lɔki so
si sɔm akara bifo;
355 tanap fɔ chia wei dɔn krik-krak
fɔl insai do fɔ dɛm bak.
Do di kɔva ɔl dɛm bon,
tɔn dɛm laik Babanki Ston.
Masa Beka kam bak kwik:
360 sabi fain di boi dɛm trik.
Wan, tu, tri, laik shut fɔ gɔn
tu boi fɔ tu brɛd bin tɔn.
Faia stil di soso hɔt,
Beka put dɛm fɔ i pɔt.
365 Smɔl taim afta muf dɛm yɛt
braun an lɔng laik tu bagɛt.
Ɔl man tink: "Nau dɛm dɔng dai."
No bi so, na sɔm bik lai!
Dɛm nɛva dai, bɔt wit dɛm mɔt
370 chɔp di brɛd, mek dɛm kɔmɔt.
Masa Beka shek i hɛd:
"I really thought that they were dead."
Dis na kɔni nɔmba siks –
wɛti ɛls dis tu fit fiks?

NƆMBA SEVɛN KƆNI

375 Tar an Tava, lukɔt man,
dis kɔni na di las wan!
Sɛka wɛti dis tu bruta
kɔt sɔm hol dɛm fɔ makuta?
Luk hau Masa Fama tot
380 wan bag kɔn fɔ dis wi rot.
Bɔt i wan go, di kɔn kɔmɔt
sɔfri sɔfri fɔ bag i mɔt.
Fama stɔp, i tɔk sei "Hau!
Dis ma bag no hɛvi nau!"
385 Dɛn i hat bigin fɔ glad
wɛn i luk dɛm boi fɔ yad.
"Wup!" i kach dɛm tu fɔ bak,
trowei dɛm fɔ wan bik sak.
Fia kach Tar an Tava smɔl:
390 Fama man bin ful dɛm ɔl,

Max na Moritz tu i pilim
hangri na kaikai i laik stilim.
Tasol beka, taim i pinis wok,
em i pasim dua long lok.
345 Tupela manki i painim rot,
go insait long hul bilong smok.
Tupela i pundaun – krak!
Olosem kotkot tupela i blak.
Puf! i pundaun nau long plaua!
350 Tupela senisim kala nau, a?
Tupela i wait olsem kambang,
i gat luk olosem dewel-man!
Tupela nau switbret i painim
long bet we beka i bin lainim.
355 Stul i bruk, na Max na Moritz
pundaun long samting olsem poris.
Samting bilong bret, ol i kolim do –
tupela nau i sori mo!
Beka i kambek – o tarangu!
360 Tupela manki biskit tru!
Wantu! dispela beka yet
rolimapim olsem bret.
Aven i hat yet, yu lukim –
beka nau tupela i kukim!
365 I dan pinis, i pulim bek;
tupela i braun olsem kek.
Husat i tingting manki i dai?
Nogat ia! Yu no ken krai.
Sel bilong biskit em i swit,
370 tupela i suim long strongpela tit!
Beka i lukim, i singaut: 'He!'
tasol tupela i ronewe.
Trik namba sikis i go pas,
trik namba seven, em i las.

LAS TRIK

375 Max na Moritz, nau mi sori!
Em las trik nau mi stori.
Tasol bilong wonem tupela katim
hul long bek na bagarapim?
Wanpela wokman, nem Meke tasol,
380 i litimapim bek long sol.
Tasol ol kon i stap insait
i ronaut long hul long baksait.
Em i ting: 'Bek i no hevi';
i lukluk raun na em i save.
385 Em i lukim tupela i sindaun
insait long ol kon i bin pundaun.
Wantu! tupela manki i stap long glasim,
em i putim long bek na pasim.
Max na Moritz, ai i raun,
390 i kamap long faktori long taun.

"Maanin, Milla! Beg yuh grine
dis-ya bagful nice an fine!"
"Shob dem een!" Im pack de trough
tight-tight so dem kyaan get aaf.
395　SQUEAKY-SQUAWKY! Koo de mill
grine dem small-small into pill!
Massa Milla hongry duck
nyam dem op an bless dem luck.
When troo tong de news did gaan,
400　people yeye dry like parch-caan.

Dᴇ H'Eɴ

Hear Miss Bolt, wha kyaan mash h'ants:
"Dem did uova lov tek chance!"
Bock seh: "True wod! Life kyaan spen
in pure rudeness widout h'en!"
405　Teacha Lampel den insis:
"Every⁄yout mus learn fram dis."
Bieka talk seh: "Certain kiek
boun fi gi yuh belly-ache!"
Nice Oncle Joe seh: "See ow
410　ronnin juok kyan spwile yuh now!"
But de Faama in im ead
tink: "Me no kya ef dem dead."
All de districk sing fa jay
talkin bout de two bad bway:
415　"Lawd be praise! Now we kyan res
afta all dem wickedness!"

"Masta mila, kam ya, man!
Yu kin gren dis kwik kwik wan?"
"Yu jɛs tɔn dɛm insay ya."
Na insay di mashin ma
395　i dɔmp di tu ɔntoum
Di mil de gren "grim gram grum"
Luk ya, yu kin stil si dɛm.
Dɛm dɔn gren pis pis lɔng tɛm.
Bɔt bifo tɛm go tu fa
400　Bra mila dɔks it dɛm ma!

Kɔɴᴋʟᴜᴢʜɔɴ

Wɛn vilej gɛt fɔ yɛri
nɔbɔdi sɛf nɔ sɔri.
Kwayɛt Mami Bolt tɔk am
se "Luk a bin dɔn si am."
405　"O yes", Masta Bil tek ɔp:
"ɛnti dɛm tu ɔnbrɔtɔp!"
Dɛn Ticha Lampɛl im se
"Luk ɔda ɛgzampul de!"
"Fɔ tru", di beka se, "bo,
410　wetin mek wi bigyay so?"
Ol Ɔnkul Frits, da gud man,
se "na so styupid jok tan."
Ɛn di ɔnɛs fama tink,
"we mi bisin if dɛm sink?"
415　Ɛn fɔ kɔt lɔng mata shɔt,
jɔy de na ɔl man im mɔt.
"Tɛl Gɔd tɛnki dɛm dɔn fri,
raskɛl dɔn, dɛm dɔn gladi."

Go fɔ mil, tɔk: "Grainam ɔl.
Duam kwik. No lɛf no smɔl."
Masa mila no di slak,
wantaim tro dɛm ɔt fɔ sak.
395 Boi dɛm go fɔ ɔnda ston
wei i grain dɛm ɛvri bon.
Wɛn di ston dɛm finish stɔp
Tar an Tava tɔn laik chɔp.
Masa mila dɔk dɛm kam,
400 chɔp di pispis fine pas yam.

FINISH

Nɛks dei wɛn di pipul hia
no man no bigin fɔ fia.
Mami Bol i gut-hat tru:
"No bi a bin tɔk fɔ yu?"
405 "Yɛs," wi Masa Kojo sei:
"Bad wɔk gɛt i on bad pei."
Pa Matyu bin nak dɛm sin:
"Bad pei kam fɔ bad pikin."
Beka man bin tɔk: "Wehele,
410 man go sɔfa fɔ i bele."
Pa Mangan bin tɔk sei: "Fɔni,
dis di ɛn fɔ ɔl dɛm kɔni."
Bɔt di fama wit drai ai:
"Mi," i tɔk, "a glad dɛm dai."
415 Fɔ kɔntri nau ɔl man dei so
dɛm rili glad di pikin go:
"Mek wi prea fɔ Tata wɛl –
Tar an Tava go fɔ hɛl."

'He, pren', Meke i tok, 'yu stap?
Wilwilim samting hia mi gat!'
Faktori man i no slek
long wilwil i kapsaitim bek.
395 Rikiraki! tupela i pilim
wil bilong wilwil i wilwilim.
Nau yu lukim tupela i stap
olsem kon, long smolpela hap!
Tupela i pinis – ating mobeta
400 pato i kaikai ologeta.

PINIS

Nius i kamap long Post-Courier,
ol pipel no seksek o guria.
Meri Bolte i autim lap:
'ating samting olosem i mas kamap'.
405 Bok i tok: 'Gutpela ia, man!
Em i pinis bilong ol giaman!'
Tisa Lempel i tokaut strong:
'This is what comes of doing wrong'.
Beka i tok: 'Mi sori mi slek
410 long mekim tupela i kamap kek!'
Na kandere tu i tok i spik:
'Pinis bilong ol longlong trik'.
Na wokman Meke i stap plei kas,
i tok tasol: 'Gau ta lasi!'
415 Olsem husat i harim stori,
i no gat wanpela i save sori.
I tok tasol: 'Pinis bilong kranki
pasin bilong tupela manki!'

MAC OND MAURIS,

mānwyrhtena wōhsong on seofon
fyttum, ðe wæs ærest on Ealdseaxna
geþēode funden ond is nū þurh
wisne wealhstōd on ūre āgen
gereord gewend

THE GESTES
OF MAK AND MORRIS

Forespǣc

Hwæt! Wē hȳraþ oft of cildum
ungehȳrsumum ond wildum!
Ēac of Max ond Mauris twǣm,
yfelwyrhtum wyrstum bǣm,
5 þā þe wīsdōmes ne rōhton
nā on gōdum weorcum þōhton,
ac geworhton synn ond leahtor,
mǣndon hospword, gilp ond hleahtor.
Ēala! Gīfre is ond rǣde
10 cild tō dōnne unrihtdǣde!
Lēode hȳnan, hundas cwellan,
æpplas, pere, plūme stelan,
gifþ heom bliss ond māran wynn,
cwēmra þyncð heom nīþ ond synn,
15 þonne on cyrce oððe scōle
sittan stille on heardum stōle.
Ac gebroc hīe ofercōm
– wālāwā! – ond atol dōm.
Gēomor wæs ond wōh ond strang
20 bēgra bearna endegang.
Forþȳ hira mān ond wīte
ic ātæfre nū ond wrīte.

Listneth lordes to my tale
how two boyes come to bale!
Bet is than romaunce of prys
of Horn the child or Ypotis,
5 Sir Topas or Pleindamour –
two of wile bare the flour
that men dyd Mak and Morris calle:
Yuil weird hem gan bifalle!
They ne herde the ioyful steuen
10 callyng synners vp to heuen;
holy men they louwe to scorn –
Day the hour that they were born!
Lither laddes al to yerne
synnen openly and derne:
15 Troublen folk, tormenten deres,
stelen apples, plowmes, peres
liketh bet than on a stole
sitten faste in chirche or scole.
But alas! For to hem bo
20 the latter ende of ioye is wo!
Horribly (is noght to layne)
endeth this mater of Almayne.
Thus with peyntures and in ryme
is descryued al hir crime.

MAK AND MOREIS

Ane lounis taill disponit in til sevyn japis
beand heireftir versit in Scottis toung
be Ioh. H. Maior.

A! Quhow comounlie men lernis
Bruitt or taill off curssit bairnis!
Tak exampill be their twa
Men couth Mak and Moreis ca,
5 Quha, declynand to convert
Til vertew be sagis airt,
Wald in secreit aften flyte
Quther lauch at thame in spyte.
Evyn til sic wantown glaikis
10 Buskit aye war thir twa smaikis!

Faschyng man and greiffyng beist,
Reiffyng apillis, peiris neist –
Thir beis boun the mair til pleiss,
Beand gert with grettar eiss,
15 Nor til lout in kirk or schuill
Modastlie on bink or stuill.
Bot alace, alace, alace,
Quha foirseis quhow endis this case!
A! Ill wes it til indure
20 Mak and Moreis quhow thai fure.
Quhairfor al thare deidis fel
I sal heir depik and tel.

Sēo Fyrmeste Fytt

Monig mon mid woruldcare
gȳmð his dēoran henneware.
25 Fyrst, menn fretað mid gefēan
ǣgru, þisse care lēan.
Ōþer, līciað eallum monnum
bridda līc on brǣdeponnum.
þridda, lofað henne ēac
30 sē ðe heora feðera brēac:
on þām pylwum hīe ā wearme
scyldað menn from cyle ond hearme.
Lōciað hēr wudwe Balde,
sēo ðe nolde licgan calde.
35 Henna þrēo wæs hire flocc
ond ān wlonca, beorhta cocc.
Smēadon swican hū hīe mihton
dēofoldǣda cyste dihtan.
Snūde curfon cnafan cāfe
40 fēower bitan from þām hlāfe,
snidon swicollīce snǣde,
tȳgdon hīe mid þynnum þrǣde,
eall gelīcost Crīstes rōde,
firenwyrhtan weargum mōde.
45 Searocræft hīe legdon dūne
on þæs gōdan wīfes tūne.
þā sē cocc þā wist geseah
hlūde song – hē þæs gefeah!
Hona crēow – cōmon mid glīwe,
50 tac, tac, tac, his mæccan trīwe.
Swealh sē cocc mid wēagesīðe
gīfre ānne cruman blīðe.

The Firste Geste

25 Many folkes taken kepe
of hir volatyles hepe:
For hir eyren ben good mete
norissyng eek for to ete.
Second cause, now and then
30 liketh folke a roosted hen.
And hir fethren doon no harme
kepe thee queme in bed and warme.
Loo, here widwe Boltes image,
that hated chile in her age.
35 Hennes three were her meynee
and a cok was gent and free.
Mak and Morris thoughten sone
what for lither thyng to done.
Faste with sleighte cutten brede,
40 bounden morsels to a threde
lyk a croys and layn with gynne
thilke trap the yerd withynne.
Whan this spied Chauntecleer
he crew loude – nas his peer;
45 with a chuk he gan hem calle:
flewn his paramoures alle,
swalwed now with haste and greed
ech a bit and toke noon heed.

The Formaist Jayp

Mekill pynis hes monie ane
With his fedderit freindis tane;
25 For thare eggis in sum wayis
Quhilk thir fowlis in yairdis layis,
Vthirwayis for that men moist
Glaidlie choppis ane chikyn roist.
Thrid, ane poynt quhairoff tak noit,
30 For thare plumage wele devoit
Til thir beddingis moniefauld,
For folk wald nocht lie on cauld.
Loe heir wedo Bauties heid,
Quha wald nocht lie swa in deid.
35 Scho had hennis, thrie in al,
And ane braw cok, fair him fal!

Mak and Moreis bath thegiddir
Quhat ado bigouth condiddir.
Sune thai cuttit, ane, twa, thire,
40 Off ane breid delivrlie
Fowir loppis of equall lenth,
Lyk ane pink thai tie ilk thing
Quirrthwart, out on ane ling,
And amiddis the wedois kail –
45 Yaird thai streik the threid out hail.
This the cok can hardlue spy,
Quhan he stairtis for til cry:
"Cokmaduidill, duidill, de!"
50 Chukmachuk! Thai cum with gle.
Cok and hennis, na thing blate,
Ilk thare lop off breid thai ate;

Ac þā fuglas sōna fundon
þæt hīe bealubendas bundon.
55 Tugon hīe on ealre sīdan,
mihte ǣlc wið ōðrum cīdan.
Flicorodon ūppe hēah,
hyhton Godes help wæs nēah.
Ēala! Hangað swǣrum swōge
60 bridda dryht from drȳgum bōge.
Swēoran wurdon þynne ond longe,
ǣðmlēase mid gryresonge.
Mid þām lætemestan ǣge
dēað ālȳste fuglas fǣge.
65 Balde nū on bedde rās,
hȳrde sorhlēoð ond āgrās,
wōd of wīce, wēan on wēne –
atol gryre wearð gesēne!
"Tēaras, flōwað from þǣm ēage!
70 Ealle māðmas ðe ic smēage,
lǣnan līfes hyht ond drēam,
birð sē wyrgda dēaðes bēam!
Gēomormōd þæt sārge wīf
clycceð þone cycencnīf;
75 cyrfð hēo þone weargan sāl
ðe worhte fugla feorhgedāl.
Hātum tēarum drenceð lām
þā hēo birð þā dēadan hām.
Endad is sēo fyrste racu,
80 folgað nū sēo ōðru sacu.

But ne couden in greet wonder
50 cok and hennes now on sonder:
Forward, bakward, to and fro
toren they with grete woo,
flewen floterynge on heigh –
hopede Goddes help was neigh.
55 Weilawei! a braunche longe
made hem somwhat vp to honge.
Long and lenger wexe the throtes,
Chauntecleers and Pertelotes.
Cok and hennes with loude steuen,
60 criede to the Lord of heuen,
leyde hir alderlaste ey
and to heuen toke hir wey.
Widwe Bolte in her bour
herde in bedde this clamour,
65 stepped out in wo and fryght –
ah, she hadde a grisly syght!
"Floweth, teres, fro myn eye!
Al myn hopes ther I spie,
ah, my liues brightest dreem
70 hangyng fro this bareyn beem!"
Ful of deol the careful wyf
cluccheth now a bocher knyf,
cutteth doun the corpses dere
hangyng lyflees al yfere.
75 And the widwe stape in age
slynketh hoom to her cotage.
This was now the firste geste
hereth moo yif that you leste.

Bot cumand til thare richt mynd,
Nane off thame could fle behynd.
55 Quircross and ouirthwairt
Thai wald pull in everie airt.
Up thai flichter al on heicht.
A! It wes ane uncouth sicht!
A! Thai hing doun fra the bair
60 Beuch off trie out in the air.
And thare thrappillis fairlie thinnit,
And thare sang grew waik, and blinnit;
Ilkane hir last egg hes layin,
Nixt the deid hes swyth thame tane.
65 Wedo Bautie in hir chalmir
Heird in bed the samin clamour;

Sair foirbodand scho com out:
A! Scho had ane cairfull dout!
"Rynnis, teiris, fra myne ein!
70 Quhat my dawrit dreme hes bein,
Haill my hoip, my glamourie,
Hingis apon yon apill trie!"
Deip in duill, with cairis cauld,
Off ane gullie scho takis hauld,
75 Cuttis the deid haill fra the stringis,
Leist thai lang in publike hingis,
And with luikis lamentous
Turnis bak, and ben the hous.
Eftir this, the formaist jape,
80 Off the tothir heir the scape.

SĒO ŌÐRU FYTT

þā sēo gōde wudwe Balde
sōna ācwencte care calde,
hēo geþōhte, milde, þwǣre,
þæt sē betsta drohtað wǣre
85 gif hēo hrǣw, ðe fūlre dǣde
geonge sturfon, brūne brǣde
ond mid āre ēstas myrge,
lēofe līc on wambe byrge.
Lā! Sē sorhwylm sēað ednīwe,
90 þā hēo seah hīe blācum hīwe,
feðerlēase heorðgenēatas,
þā ðe hwīlum geardes scēatas
oft þurhflugon būton wonde,
wyrmas sōhton on þām sonde.
95 Nīwe tēar onfēhþ sēo eorðe,
ond sē hund stent bi þām heorðe.
Mac geswæhte þone brǣde.
"Ūp on þone hrōf!" hē sǣde.
þurh þæt rēchol mid gefēan
100 sēoþ hīe heora synna lēan,
æs, þām rēðan wyrdes dōm
heals ond fiðerhoman nōm.
Drēama lēas mid disce hende
Balde cleofan in āwende,
105 feccan sūran cawles dǣl,
ealra wista lēofost mǣl,
þæt hēo lufade ungemǣte
wyrmd ednīwe on heorþes hǣte.
On þām hrōfe hrōre ond cwice
110 hennebanan worhton swice.

THE SECONDE GESTE

Whan the peyne bigon to esen
80 Bolte thoghte herself to plesen,
wende it myght be for the beste
putte the corpses now to reste,
rooste the martirs al at ones,
or boille hem with the marybones,
85 with honour to passe the hote
deyntee morsels thurgh her throte.
Reed the thoghtes on her face:
"Requiescant dum in paunche!"
But renewed was her care
90 when she seigh hem deed and bare,
hulde and nakede on the herthe,
fowles that whilom in the erthe
scracchynge, scrycchynge wormes soghte,
neuere of hir ende thoghte.
95 Ah, the widwe wop and cride
Pluto standyng bi her side.
Mak and Morris smelte the brede,
vp on to the roof they yede.
Thurgh the chymney with glade mode
100 they behoolde the freely fode,
heedlese hennes, broune and wanne,
hissynge, fryenge in the panne.
Bolte wente with a bole
for to fecche som soured cole:
105 liked hir best of al hir mete
warmed ayen in mene hete.
Loo! thise hennicides slye
bisy on the roof on hye!

THE TOTHIR JAYP

Quhan guid wedo Bautie syne
Fra hir ein had dicht the bryne,
Quir in hir mynd scho turnit,
Quhow hir freindis that scho murnit,
85 Quhilk unitmouslie war gane,
Best be schervit, gin alane
Scho wald geiff thame mensk in peice,
And consume thame roist in greise.
Yit hir playnt wes na thing slaikit,
90 Quhan scho saw thame bair and nakit,
Plukkit haill apon the harth,
Quha in yaird, and als in garth,
Umquhyll in thare pryme off day
Blisfullie wald scraip and play.

95 A! The wedo greitis eft;
Pom the doig hir nevir left.
Mak and Moreis smelt the reik.
"Up!" On to the ruift thai seik.
Dount the chimla, ouirjoyit,
100 Thai persaiff the hennis deployit,
Quha, off hals and heid dispuilyit,
Braw abune the ingill bruilyit.
To the laich hous with ane assit
Hes the wedo Bautie passit,
105 With intent off sautit kail
Hir ane ladillful to wail,
Off the quhilk scho maist wes fane,
Quhan it wes hett ouir agane.
Al this quhyle thai war abuif
110 Besie wirkand on the ruif.

Mac mid listum foreþōhte,
nytwyrðlīcne angel brōhte.
Sēoþ on wundorlīcre wīsan
fyrstan henne ūp ārīsan!
115 Ōðru fylgað hire swyfte,
þridda fugol is on lyfte,
feorða stīgð nū ūp sē cocc –
angelcynn hæfð ealne flocc!
þā hie hōfon hāte hūþe
120 bearc sē hund mid hlūdum mūþe,
ac þā þēofas, rēaf on honde,
læfdon stōwe heora sceonde.
Hrēam þǣr bið, be mīnre sāwle!
Lā, sēo cwene cymð mid cawle.
125 Swīgde ond geswearc mid swǣre
þā hēo seah þā pannan – lǣre!
Hȳðd wæs hire heorðes hord –
"Fretol hund!" þæs wīfes word.
"Grim untȳdre, lāþ ond hēan,
130 nū onfēhstū rihtlīc lēan!"
Ond mid hlædle, cēne ond snel,
hēo ābiett þæs hundes fel.
Hlūde wrēgþ hē þās unhylde –
Hē wāt hē is būton scylde.
135 Hæleþ hilð sēo hecge grēne –
nāht of briddum nys gesēne
būton heora sceancan twēgen,
henneslagna hildesegen.
Endad is sēo ōðru racu,
140 folgað nū sēo þridde sacu.

Mak the steler quik of thoght
110 hath an angle rod ybroght;
wirchyng craftily and harde:
the firste hen goth heuenward.
Heue and ho! another, gory,
riseth vp fro purgatory!
115 Vp the thirde fleeth sans fethren,
now the ferthe seekth hir brethren.
Wacchyng this the dogge vnslowe
berked loude and schille "bow-wowe".
But the boyes with hir theft
120 for the forest hauen left.
Of deol and peyne of oother men
they yeue noght a pulled hen.
Stryf I see and heuy mournyng:
Loo, here widwe Bolt retournyng;
125 bolt vpright, so stood she thanne
lokynge on the empty panne.
Al the hennes disapperd!
"Pluto!" first her cri was herd.
"Pluto! Ah, thou helle hound,
130 tak thee bak to helle ground!"
Beet him with a spoon ful smerte,
sans conscience and tendre herte.
Loude he gan to yelle and wayle,
Bolte claght hym bi the tayle.
135 Vnder hegge, loo! thise tweyne
snoren dremynge of Cokayne.
Of hir feest is now alone
vysybul oon chiken bone.
Wole ye any more of it?
140 Folweth now the thridde fit.

Mak had als with greit foirthocht
Rodd and ling and angill brocht.
Quhippmaquhapp! Up throuch the lum
Chikyn nowmer ane is cum.
115 Quhippmaquhapp! Cummis nowmer twa.
Item, nowmer thrie alswa.
Now the laif, with nowmer fowir:
Quhippmaquhapp! Al in thare powar!
Pom biheld thare deidis grouff,
120 And he berkis: "Youff, youff, youff!"
Bot the pair off thame ful gay
Doun descendit, and away.
A! This bodis stryff and stour,
For the wedo makis retour.
125 Stound scho stude in to the rowme,
Quhan scho saw hir pan wes towme.

Haill hir poultrie playne wes gane:
"Pom!" – That wurd scho fand alana.
"A! Thou, Pom, thou pround poultroun!
130 I sal leit the, limmer loun!"
With the ladill lang and lairge
Scho gaiff litill Pom his chairge,
Quhais lament can loudlie lilt,
For he wist he had na gilt.
135 Mak and Moreis, under foillage,
Snorkis sweit apon thare spoillage,
And off al thare bankett blithe
Na thing but twa schankis kithe.
Eftir this, the tothir jaip,
140 Off the thrid heir now the scaip.

SĒO ÞRIDDE FYTT

Cnēowon alle menn on londe
Cuþbeorht cræftigne of honde.
Worhte Cuðþbeorht betstan wǣde,
syrcas siowian wæs rǣde,
145 cūðe scyrtan oððe lengan,
smicru scrūd mid bordan glengan,
worhte brēc ond wearme pāde
ǣlcre ylde, ǣlcum hāde.
Weorc mid scēarrum ond mid nǣdle
150 wrēah from wræce him ond wǣdle.
Cwæð þæt weorcdǣd mon ne scende –
sticcian wæs his līfes ende.
Gif þīn hemeþe sīe tōtoren,
of þām rocce cnoppa loren,
155 ge behindan ge beforan –
bring þæt hrægl þām nǣdlboran!
Forþȳ menn on būre ond healle
wǣron ā his winas ealle.
Ac þā þwēoran cnafas þōhton
160 hū hīe wā ond gnorn him brōhton.
Hwæt! Beforan Cuddes bytle
ran mid rāre riþ unlȳtle.
Lǣt sum brycg unbrǣcu ond brād
secgas ofer swonnes rād.
165 Mac ond Mauris būton ege
gyrwdon þisses wyrhtan slege:
Hīe mid sage snidon hraþe
cleofunge on þām paðe.
Æfter māne cild ungōde
170 hrȳmdon bēgen ofermōde:

THE THRIDDE GESTE

Lordynges, herkneth to my tale,
murier than the nightyngale!
In vilage and in toun
Buk the taylor had renoun.
145 Jupes, hosen, habergeounes,
werkday eek and Sunday gownes,
clokes, skirtes for to maken
taylor Buk wold soon ontaken;
or he wold perchance eek knowen
150 how t'amenden, cutten, sowen,
fastnen botouns of al kynd,
forn, biside and eek bihynd –
al this werk, performed blyue,
was the purpos of his lyue.
155 Therfore folk in his vilage
were his freendes of eche age.
But the lither felouns thoghte
how they hym to sorwe broghte.
Fel that Bukkes hous bifore
160 a wylde noisy treem dyd rore.
Ore the water is a plank
ledeth men fro bank to bank.
Mak and Morris with a sawe
faste thoghte a play to plawe:
165 priuely they sawe a cleft
til nat muchel boord was left.
Whan that lither deed was done
hokreden the boyes sone:

THE THRID JAYP

Until nane in toun wes fremmit
Ane, the quhilk wes Bukkie nemmit.
Oukda, gounis, sunda clokis,
Breikis, trewis, and cuttit frokis,
145 Claithis wth pokis and cravattis,
Mantillis, justicotis, spattis –
Til mak sic habuilyiment
Tailyior Bukkie wes intent.
War thare quhat for til repair,
150 For til schort, translait, or gair,
Geiff ane knap war off the hois
Lows or limp, als I suppois,
Quhow and quhair, or in, or out,
Foir or aft, thare wes na dout:

155 Maister Bukkie wald it sort,
For this wes his lyffis support.
Thairfor ilkane off the toun
Wes in kyndnes til hem boun.
Mak and Moreis, thai alane
160 Ettillit to caus him payn.
For nei by the tailyouris plais
Ran ane wattir in ane rais.
Quir it, ane brig can leid,
Quhairatour folk micht proceid.
165 Mak and Moreis, na thing slaw,
Hakkit hidlingis with ane saw,
Malingynous, quhischmaclink!
In the samin brig ane chink.
Quhan thir thingis war enakkit,
170 Men micht heir ane suddan rakkit:

"Hē, cum ūt nū, sott ond slāw,
sēamere, i-āw, i-āw!"
Hē geþyldig drēogan mihte
husc ond hōl ond word unrihte,
175 ac þæs dolan assan naman
geaf him ierre, torn ond graman.
Ond mid elne springð hē snelle
þæt þā yflan cild hē cwelle,
forðon bearn ednīwan, efne!
180 hoceriað mid assan stefne.
Cūþbeorht cēne stōp tō fyhte –
Hwæt! Brycg brosnað from gewihte,
ond mid bearna hlūdum hrēame
sāh sē sēamere on þām strēame.
185 þā sē brimgiest won wið flōde
cōmon gōs ond gandra gōde.
Heora sceancan Cūþbeorht ēaðe,
flotmonn læhte, forht for dēaðe;
bēgen fæste on his hondum
190 flēag hē ūp from ȳþgeblondum.
Wæt ond cyle, þæt ic dēme,
bēoþ þām monnum nōht gecwēme.
Forðȳ rinc, fornēah ofslagen,
fēlde sārnesse on his magan.
195 Ac his wifes lof sīe sungen:
Hæted īsern hēo hæfþ brungen,
ðe, gesett on caldum þearmum,
hredde hlāford cræftum wearmum.
Ceasterware cȳþdon stunde:
200 "Hāl is Cūþbeorht from þām sunde."
Endad is sēo þridde racu,
folgað nū sēo fēorþe sacu.

"Hey, com out now tayler Buk,
170 tayled tayler, muk, muk, muk!"
Taylor Buk coude beer a deel
patient and meek and leel,
but who gan hym 'tayled' calle,
wolde hym clawe on the galle.
175 With a yerdstik Buk ful wood
sterted out to kille the brood.
Krak! with dyn as loud as thonder
al the brigge brast on sonder.
Soon was herd "muk, muk!" again,
180 plop! the taylor's doun the drain.
Loo! his feet ben seen per chaunce.
Mak performed a morris daunce.
Whan Buk dronken hadde his draughte
in despair for help he raughte.
185 In eche hoond a gooses shanke
he fleigh vp on to the banke.
Buk, thus neigh ybroght of dawe,
felt some peynes in his mawe.
But his wyues craft be praised!
190 She a pressyng iren saised:
the cause of his maladye
was moist and coold, she hoot and drye
hete on his woombe dighte,
putte the coolde humours righte.
195 Twys a goos hym saued ethe
fro the pose, quakke, and dethe.
Soon the rumour wide sproong
"Buk is hool again and stroong!"
Mak we mery, haue we blis,
200 Was the thridde fit ywis.
Yeue the mynstrel breed and ale
and go forward with the tale!

"Yee, cum out, ye billie-buk!
Tailyour, tailyour, guk, guk, guk!"
Ilk injure micht Bukkie thoill,
And off selff na tyne controill,
175 Bot quhan sic ane strain he heirit,
Sair aganis the grain it steirit.
Tyt he lowpis with his wand
Fra the thressald off his land,
For off new with dreid him struk
180 Loud and cleir thare "Guk, guk, guk!"
Swyth he til the brig is gane,
Crak! The brig is cleft atwain.
"Guk, guk, guk!" agane resounis.
Splischmasplasch! The tailyour drounis.
185 At the nik, quhan this wes dun,
Thir twa geis haiff hiddir wun;

Quhame, in feir off deidis jawis,
Bukkie cleikis be thare clawis;
And with geis in baith his neiffis
190 Flotterand the dry retreiffis.
Mairatour, als thairanent,
Sic thing geiffis nane eisament:
Loe, quhow Bukkie hentis hame
With ane wafull warkand wame.
195 Praysit be his guidwyff Bukkie!
Quha with hir hait im wes lukkie,
Quhilk on his cauld wame impressit
Hes the scaith als tyt redressit.
Sune the toun quod, ane be ane:
200 "Bukkies hairt is hale agane!"
Eftir this, the thrid off jaypis,
Heiris quhow the ferd escaypis.

Sēo Feorþe Fytt

Ælcum menn, ge meowle ge beorne,
hofað þæt hē āwuht leorne:
205 Nā þæs ᚠᚾᚻᚠᚱᛚ es stæfgedræg
monnes mynd getimbran mæg;
nā mæg wrītan, tellan, rǣdan
āna monnes wīsdōm brǣdan.
Rīm ond stǣr ond swēges cræft
210 lǣdaþ menn on woruldes hæft.
Forðȳ ēac þæs Ēcan lāre
hȳre monn mid trȳwre āre.
Tendan wel þæt heofonliht
wæs þæs līðan Lamples riht.
215 Ac þām bearnum – mīnum aþe! –
wǣron lār ond lārēow lāþe.
Lā! þām wyrstan yfeldǣdan
mæg nān lārēow nāht rǣdan.
Nū þām secge smēocan lyste,
220 hē gefeah ā wyrta cyste,
þēawe, ðe æfter dæges swince
riht is þæt wē ealdum rince
willes unnon hēhstre wynne,
ealra synna lǣstre synne.
225 Ac þā swican wǣron gearwe
unrihtdǣde ond bealusearwe:
Smēadon hwæþre þurh his pīpan
lāðne lārēow mihton grīpan.
Hwīlum þā on Sunnannihte
230 Lampel sæt ond songas dihte,
organan on swōtum swēge
hlynsodon mid glīwgefēge,

The Ferthe Geste

Tis an olde and wise decree:
men mote lerne the A.B.C.
205 But to lerne, spelle, write,
ryme and per chaunce endite,
lerne gramer and acountes,
names of bestes, erbes, mountes,
can a mannes soul nat saue –
210 ryghtful faith eek moot he haue.
Thus thurgh errours loothsom night
Lampels lamp shoon cleer and bright.
He wolde, othres wit to eche,
gladly lerne and gladly teche.
215 Mak and Morris louede hym ille,
thoghte his techyng worth a fille.
Now this techer had greet nede
smokyng the tobako wede
(thilke newe worldes plante)
220 which, though synful, we mowe grante
after dayes swynkyng sore
to an olde man and hore.
Mak and Morris wole nat blynne;
hoker thenchen they with gynne,
225 thoghte to doon the techer shame:
made hym thurgh his pipe to grame.
Fel that on a messe day
whan he wonte was to playe
th'orgon murie in the chirche,
230 sat and gan his musik wirche,

The Ferd Jayp

Ane law rynnis ouralquhare:
Man maun leir ane halesum lare.
205 Nocht the abece alane
Puttis him on ane hiear plane;
Nocht alane to reid and wryte
Makis ane man off skil perfyte;
Nocht alane to lay ane compt
210 Maun ane prudent man be prompt,
Bot alswa til sage doctryne
Blisfullie his eir inclyne.
For the quhilk, be wys entent,
Doctour Lampill wes present.
215 Vntill Mak and Moreis baith
For that ressoun he wes laith;

For quha dois ignominie
Heidis nocht the dominie.
Now sett this guid clerk and wys
220 Be tabacco mekill prys,
Quhilk diversioun, nocht to layne,
Eftir dargis ploy and payne
Til ane kyndlie guid auld man
In his hairt resent, quha can?
225 Mak and Moreis, nocht to stynt,
At ane mirrie meinis can mynt,
Quhow be his deir pyp thai micht
Him ane dynt in dernë dicht.
Aince, quhan sabboth com about,
230 And Dan Lampill, dous, devout,
With ane fervour in the kirk
Gert his organe pibroch wirk,

        sluncon sliðan þa unholde
        tō þæs mildan monnes bolde.
235 Mac þā mǣre pīpan fond,
        fæste hire fēhð his hond.
        Mauris drægð from dyrnum poccan
        atol ligetmelwes croccan,
        and hē snūde būtan hylde
240 þǣre pīpan hēafod fylde.
        Nū his hūs hīe lǣfað snelle:
        mæssan ende cȳðð sēo belle.
        Efne Lampel rōw ond dæfte
        lēac þæt cyrcegeat mid cræfte.
245 Nū þæt song ond swēg æt ende
        Lampel milde ond smylte wende
        mid his ymnere under earme
        hāmweard on his bytle wearme.
        Lārēow wæs rihte on sælde,
250 þā hē his rēcelsfæt onǣlde.
        "Ā!", cwæð hē, "þæt hēhste gōd
        is clǣne mynd ond orsorg mōd!"
        Wumm!! Sēo pīpe bearst mid dyne,
        swefles stence ond Etnes bryne;
255 ofen, crocc ond wætercetel,
        blæcern, rēcfæt, restesetl –
        wumm!! on flyhte eall his æhte
        mid þundorrāde ond ligetslæhte.
        þā sē smoca ūpp āstāh
260 Lampel ðe on flette sāh
        cwicne syhstu – Gode þonc! –
        ac his scēne hlēor gescronc:

        thise two boyes slye and connynge
        cropen in the techers wonynge
        wher the bigge pipe stoond.
        Mak heeld faste in his hoond.
235 Morris gan a botel gripe,
        poured pouder in the pipe.
        Swifte as swalwes hoom they wende
        for the messe is at ende.
        Lampel calm and tired sore
240 lokketh now the chirche dore,
        gan with book and musik quaire
        gladly to his hous repaire.
        For to resten he hym dyghte,
        thankfully his pipe lighte.
245 "Ah" quoth he "ther is no plesure
        lyk contentment in your lesure".
        Bum! the pip fleeth in a glare
        with a dyn coude mauments scare.
        Quen, ynkhorn and his chair
250 al go flyenge thurgh the air.
        Whan the smook was blown away
        Lampel lay – God blesse the day –
        liuyng whan the noyse stynte,
        but was brused from the dynte.

        Baith thir lounis on braid wald creip
        In his hous and hal to peip
235 Quhair his pyp of meirskum standis;
        Mak it hes intil his handis;
        Moreis in his pouch hes borne,
        And tane out, ane pouldar horne,
        And in les nor onie tyme
240 Pouldar in the pyp can pryme.
        Hamewart now, be craft, but faill!
        For the kirk bigynnis to skaill.
        At this hour, meik and demure,
        Lampill lokkis the vestrie dure;
245 And with kie and musik skoiris,
        Lowssit from officialll choiris,
        Ioiouslie, with heid on loft,
        Cayris til his couthie croft.

        Syne, bigane with gratitude,
250 Smoiking off his pyp renued.
        "A!" quod he, "The greitest blis
        Is contentment sweit, iwis!"
        Quhrang! His pyp on suddane brast
        With ane brall and balefull blast.
255 Coffa pott and wattir glas,
        Ink, tabacco buist, and vas,
        Stowfe and buird and elbok chayr –
        Al flagratis with feirfull flayr.
        Quhan the reik and vapour rase,
260 Lampill wes, be Goddis grase,
        Left on lyff, yit on his bak:
        Chaffar deir coft with the crak!

Nosu, ēaran, hnol and hond
blace bærnde bǣl ond brond:
265 wæs his hēafod myrce mǣld
ond þæs hǣres lāf forswǣld.
Hwā sceal nū þā cildru lǣran,
rimgetæl ond þylcræft mǣran?
Hwā is ðe on scōle ond cyrce
270 ambiht ond his symbel wyrce?
Hwæt is þǣre pīpan notu?
Lōciað þa lȳtlan brotu!
Ǣlc þing sōna bið gehǣld –
ac þæt rēcfæt nǣfre onǣld!
275 Endad is sēo fēorðe racu,
folgað nū sēo fifte sacu.

Sēo Fifte fytt

Gif þin ēam, ge earm ge rīce,
bīde nēah on þām wīce,
bēo geþwǣre ond ā līðe:
280 þæt gelicað ēame swīðe.
"Gōdne morgen!" bēod him swǣse;
fricg him: "Wæs sēo niht getǣse?"
Bring þām aldan lēofan rince
ēstas, sēlest wist mid drince.
285 Gif his hneccan oððe hrycg
bīte ceafor oððe mycg,
help þām mǣge – swā ic dēme:
nefa bēo þām ēame cwēme.
Georne his bebodu lǣste.
290 Gif hē fnēse myclum fnæste

255 Nose, hoondes, face and ere
lyk a blomans neb appere
and the rest of haires broune
burned to ashes on his croune.
Who shal now the childer techen
260 and the hoord of wisdom echen?
Who shal doon now Lampels werke
as a scryuener and clerke?
Wherfrom shal the techer smoken
now his pipe is al tobroken?
265 Time wol helen euery wound –
but the pipe ne werth nat sound.
Lat us of the ferthe blynne
and the fifte geste bigynne!

The Fifte Geste

Who in burugh or vilage
270 hath an uncle oold of age
curteis be and of seruise
that som profit myght arise.
Bryng hym what hym liketh haue:
drynke, mete, knyf to shaue;
275 yif par chaunce on his rygge
biteth hym a flee or migge,
be ful gladly alwey yare
to releuen uncles care;
yif the uncle harde fnese
280 wyshe hym to fele at ese;

Fyngirris, face, and fisnomie
War ane blak anatomie,
265 And hias henmaist heid off hair
Al forbrunt for evirmair.
Quha sal furth instruk the bairnis?
Quha tin sciens sett up cairnis?
Quha in Doctour Lampillis steid
270 Sall the lade off office leid?
Quha sal yit tabacco bruik,
Quhan the pype hir selff bituik?
Althing sall, quhan tym is ryp,
Curit be, outtane the pyp.
275 Eftir this, the ferd off jaypis,
Heiris quhow the fift escaypis.

The Fift Jape

Quha in burch or upaland
Eme or unkill hes to hand,
Lat him kurtase be and kynd
280 For til pleisour unkillis mynd.
In the morn thou speke: "Gud da, schir!
Beis that quhairwith you to pay, schir?"
Fynd him quhat him list, the quhyle:
Papyer, pyp, and tapour spyle.
285 Or giff sumquhair in his bak
Ocht wald wark or yuik or thwak,
Ythand be, and amyabill,
Obsequent and servisabill.
Or giff eme tak heland sneischan
290 For til neise, with noyis onleischan,

wysc him Godes help ond hǣlþe –
sie sē ēam ā on sǣlþe.
Gif hē cyme hām on nihte
nim gescȳ from caldum cnihte,
295 gif him hōd ond pāde wearme –
hē sīe on Abrahames bearme!
Blissie his ēam sē nefa:
trēowe ond līðe bēo his sefa.
þǣra lāðra bearna tēam
300 lȳtel lufade *heora* ēam.
þencað hwylce lǣwe ond swice
beornas worhton Frēoðurice!
Cūþ is wide ǣlcum secge
ceafor brūn on holte ond hecge;
305 dēor ðe crēopað þurh þā telgan
syhstu lēaf ond wǣstm swelgan.
Beornas from þæs bēames foldan
scōcon bitelan on moldan.
þæt þā crēoperas flēon ne mihton
310 nearu cearcern hīe heom dihton.
Of mid ēfste, ond gelōme
on þæs ēames beddes glōme!
Sōna Fredi mēðe ond rōwe
hōdod sōhte restestōwe,
315 lēac his ēagna hlidu – efne!
smylte fnærð on swǣsum swefne.
Crupon þā from beddes hyrnum
eorðgesceaft mid brūnum byrnum.
Sēoþ þā frecan sceadugengan
320 tō þæs ēames nose tengan!

whan he cometh hoom at night
doffe hos bootes anonright,
fecche gis goune eek and his cappe –
shiueren moot he nat by happe –
285 shortly, glad be and intent,
mak the uncle right content.
Mak and Morris likede that ille,
thoghte hir emes ioye ti spille.
Chafers ben yknowe wide
290 that in trees and hegges bide,
crepygne, crawlynge to and fro,
hondred, thousand other mo.
Mak and Morris shake with connyng
doseyns doun of hir green wonyng,
295 putten than the crawlers broune
narwely in a prisoune,
and in emes quiltes thikke
hiden they the chafers quikke.
Soon to bedde gooth eem Ion
300 with his piked nightcap on,
couereth hym, closeth his eyen,
thencheth calmly for to lyen.
But the chafers fro hir gayle
marche to eemward, heed-to-tayle.
305 Uncle sleepth in sweet repose.
Loo! a chafer hath his nose.
"Auch" he cried "what is heer?"
whan he caught the vgly deer.

Thou cry: "God you bles!" bur byde,
"Fair and favour you bityde!"
Or giff lait he hame commuitis,
Ye sal help tak off his buitis,
295 Bring him mantill, mutch, and muilis;
Luik that na the nicht him cuilis –
And, in fine, men beis attent
That the eme salbe content.
Mak and Moreis for their pairt
300 Lykit nocht the samyn airt.
Umbethink quhat evill skeme
Thai perfourmit on thare eme!
Ilk ane wate: ane littill clok-
Chafer is na thrissill cok.

305 In the grene trie, hiddir, thiddir,
He wil scrawl and skelnt and skliddir.
Mak and Moreis ful off gle
Schoggillis thame doun fra the tre.
And ilk ane his papyer pok
310 With thir sextupedis can stok.
Tharewith unto Unkill Fred
Furneiss thai his feddir bed!
Quhiddir, buskit for the nicht,
Sune he passis with ane licht;
315 Syne his ein disponis for slummyr,
Saggis, and sleipis withouten cummyr.
Bot thir chaferris, scartmascayre!
Marchis, rissin, fra thare layre.
Loe, quhow ane, that furdats gane is,
320 Unkill Freddies neis attains.

"Eoten, þyrs of Caines cynne,
scyld mē, God, from fūlre synne!"
Swifte, þæt his līf hē hredde,
sprong sē forhta secg from bedde.
325 Bāt ond stang þæt wōde swearm
ēames hrycg ond heals ond earm –
ūpp ond niðer, ongemong,
þrīstra þryccendra geþrong.
Ac sē eorl swā ōðer Herod
330 slōg untȳdra wyrged werod.
þā þæt wæl on flette crang
"Ecum Gode lof!" hē sang.
Nū þām menn sē sluma spēow.
Slēp oððæt sē hona crēow.
335 Endad is sēo fifte racu,
folgað nū sēo sixte sacu.

SēO SIXTE FYTT

þā on beorhtre Eastertīde
bæcestre ond bæceras wīde
bacað cyclas, mettas swōte,
340 hunigbære gebæc tō bōte,
Mac ond Mauris ēac þā dyrnan
swōtan ēstas woldon gyrnan.
Ac sē bæcere, frōd ond fræge,
lēac þæt bæcern wel mid cæge.
345 þēofas þā ðe cumað for stale
mōton þurh þæt rēchol smale.
Hruron hrefnas, swearte mid sōte,
þurh þæt rēcþyrl, rincas rōte.

And the eem ful sore afryght
310 lefte his bedde as fowl in flyght.
"Auch!" Ther is another paire
in his nek and in his haire;
forn, bihynde and eck biside
wlatsom chafers fleen wide.
315 Uncle Ion in this greet nede
crusheth al the chafers thede.
Loo behold! The werre is ended;
leste sayd but soon amended.
Uncle Ion now nimeth kepe
320 vndistourbled for to slepe,
slepeth al the nightertale
bet than dooth a nightyngale.
After fiue what comth nixt?
Listneth warly to the sixt!

THE SIXTE GESTE

325 Whan in ioyful estertide
pious bakers baken wide
many a swete wastelbrede,
cakes eek both white and rede,
Mak and Morris wilnede derne
330 thilke swete metes yerne.
But the baker with foresight
hath the bakhous lokked right.
Theues mote par auenter
therfor thurgh the chymney enter.
335 Loo! the boyes blakke as coles
fro hir hedes to hir soles.

"A!" he cryis, "Quhat moit I sie?"
And he grippis the scarabie.
Sie the eme with grue and scunnyr,
Off his leittacamp bed thunnyr.
325 "Owch!" – He hentis off thir burdies
On his scruff, and cuit, and hurdies.
Frount and reir and aythir hand
Crap and flappit, murmurand.
Unkill Fred, to beit this neid,
330 Straik and stampit althing deid.
A! Off al this brawl and bikkir
Restis nocht ane crawl klikkir!
Unkill Fred is redd off cummyr
And his ein inclynis to slummyr.
335 Eftir this, the fift off japis,
Heiris quhow the saxt escapis.

THE SAXT JAYP

In the peaxful tym off Pasch
Quhan thir blisset bakstaris fasch
To confectione for the maistrie
340 Succer breid and gustie paistrie,
Mak and Moreis als wald grein
Sic sweit thingis til obtein.
Bot the baiker takis cure
Makand fast the baik hous dure.
345 Thairfor quhasumeir wald theiff
Throuch the lum his peth man preiff.
Quhousch! Thai haiff thare selff deiekkit
And devaillis lyk corbies blekkit.

Puf! Hīe cumað nū to reste
350 on þæs bæceres melucieste:
Bēoð nū hwītre þonne hrīm,
morgenmeolc ond cealc ond līm.
Æses georne sēoþ hīe bord
ond þæron gebaca hord.
355 Lā! Sē stōl brycð lȳtle þrāge.
Hwæt! þā licgað hīe on dāge,
ðe hīe hylþ nū drōf ond deorc –
seoð þæt drēorge græftgeweorc!
Bæcere gīfre bearn onfond
360 þā ðe clām on clommum bond.
Snūde hē þā cnafan forhte
on tō wundorhlāfas worhte.
Ofen is gīet hāt mid fȳre –
hē hīe scȳfð on sūsles bȳre.
365 Ruf! Hē drægð from þære glēde
brūne bacene bearn gemēde.
þincstū þæt hīe wyrd forspilde?
Gīet hīe lifað, rēðe ond wilde!
Scearpum tōðum swā sēo mūs
370 fritt ælc cnafa þurh his hūs,
ond sē bæcere hrȳmde: "Sēoþ!
Bēgen beornas blīðe flēoþ!"
Endad is sēo sixte racu –
folgað nū sēo latoste sacu.

Puf! the childer come to reste
in the bakers mele cheste.
Loo! they ben vp and below
340 front and bak as white as snow.
Gladly seen they lasse than twelue
smale cakes on a shelue.
Krak! the stool brekth soon ynough.
Plop! the paire is in the dough.
345 Loo behold! the doughy pages
lyk two pitefulimages.
Ah, the master baker waccheth,
Mak and Morris and hem caccheth,
Oon, two, three! and fsate as thoght
350 hath hem on two looues wroght,
lyke a pecok, duk or drake
in breed the lither briddes to bake.
The oues is yet glowynge hoot:
in he pusheth hem, God woot.
355 Out he drawth the pastry fode
for they ben now broune and gode –
Al men thoghte they can nat thriue –
but behold, they ben aliue!
crunchy, crunch! the lither brattes
360 frete hir couer lyk two rattes.
Cried the baker "Day the day!
Bothe pastries renne away!"
Sixte geste ended faste,
sitteth stille and heerth the laste!

Quhouff! In til the kist thai pore,
350 In the quhilk is meil gallore.
Loe, quhan that thai furdar staukis
Baith thir lounis ar quhyt als caukis.
Nixt thai se with gle abufe
Sundrie succurit knottis off lufe.
355 Crak! – The chayr refuissis carriage;
Quhapp! – Thai lie in to the parrage.
Haill with drappand daich bidicht
Thai off petie ar ane sicht.
A! The baker sune apperis
360 And persaiffis the likrous feris.
Ane, twa, thrie! – afoir ye thocht,
In twa breidis he hes thame brocht.

In the oyne, quhyle that it burnis!
Quhouff! Thai flitt in ti the furneis.
365 Quhouff! Thai ar thairfra retytit;
Broun and croustie and weill fyrit.
Men thinkis, endit hes thare stryff!
Bot na! Thai ar yit on lyff.
Knybbill, knabbill! – myis fassoun
370 Be thair teith thai breik presoun.
And the maister baker cryis:
"Maircie! Thare the fellonis flyis!"
Eftir this, the saxt off jaypis,
Heiris quhow the latmaist scaypis.

Sēo Seofeþe Fytt

375 Mac ond Mauris, nū fylgð rǣde
lēan for lāðre yfeldǣde!
Nāt ic hwȳ þēos twēgen tȳde
sliton þǣra sacca hȳde.
Hwæt! þǣr birð gebūr cigd Blacc
380 on his sceoldre beresacc.
Ceorl gewāt, ac lǣfde hraðe
him behindan corna swaðe.
"Heilag þor!" hē stōd ond spæc:
"Mikel bygg rens fra þis sekk!"
385 Ac hē wlāt mid wildum torne
Mac ond Mauris on þām corne,
ond in sinne wīdan sacc,
scȳfð hē Mauris, scȳfð hē Mac.
Fyrht wæs drēfed ǣlcum beorne,
390 forðȳ ceorl hīe bær tō cweorne.
"Trygge carl, cum, tak þir sweines,
grind mid skil þeim, skin and beines!"
"Gif hīe mec!" – þe mylnweard georne
scēaf þā weargan in þā cweorne;
395 grand þā grundfūsan tō sōðum
gryreweorc mid grindetōðum.
Mylen spīwþ heom styccemǣlum –
on līfes hīwe, ac lȳtlum dǣlum.
Frǣton gēs þā dēadan guman,
400 lāðre lāfe lǣstan cruman.

The Laste Geste

365 Mak and Morris I wexe pale,
for now comth the laste tale.
Why mote thilke lither briddes
sakkes slitten right amiddes?
Look, here bereth fermour Blak
370 a sak for millyng on his bak.
He departed and ful slowe
gonnen graynes out to flowe.
Stood and wondryd: "Haly crouche!
Mikel quhet rens fra my pouche!"
375 Ha! he seeth with ioye grete
Mak and Morris in the whete.
Rabs! he shoof the yuil pak
with a shouel in his sak.
Mak and Morris wenden ille
380 beynge carried to the mille.
"Lefe milner, grind at anes
thir twa barnes skyn and banes!"
In the hopur caste he clene
thilke lither boyes bidene
385 and to smale morsels groond:
See hem deled foot and hoond.
But ful soon the gees come frete
what hem thoughte delicious mete.

The Latmaist Jape

375 Mak and Moreis, dre your weird!
Hereis your latmaist jayp in eird!
Quhairfoir nou ar thir twa frekkis
Slaschand slittis in thir sekkis?
Loe, Makkinla, in guid keltyr,
380 Turssand on his bak ane meltyr.
Skairs he warpis him about,
Quhan the girnall rynnis out.
Stound he speikis and als ane stok:
"Nyodd! Fat lichinnis aye this trok?"
385 Ha! Harrou! He seis ful fayn
Mak and Moreis in the grayn.

Quhapp! With his mault skuip he schulis
In his mekill sek thir fulis.
Mak and Moreis feilis schill,
390 For thare gait is to the mill.
"Maistir milnar! Ho! Tak tent!
Gar this grynd incontinent!"
"Aye, certayn!" And out he schaikis
In the happir thir twa smaikis.
395 Rikkillrakkill! Rikkillrakill!
Gais the mill with mekill crakkil.
Heir to kirnallis se thame ground,
Figourit in mappamound.
Bot als tyt lyk onie peise
400 Gorgis thame the milnaris geise.

SĒ ENDESTÆF

For þām dēadum fyrr ond nēar
menn ne wēopon nānne tēar.
Balde sǽde, milde ond līðe:
"Foreseah ic wyrd unblīðe."
405 Sagu wæs þām sēamere hende:
"Yfelnes nys līfes ende!"
Lampel sǽde, wīs ond frōd:
"Heora dōm is bisen gōd!"
Ac sē bæcere, fætt ond þwǽre,
410 fand þæt mon tō fretol wǽre.
Eam geþōhte: "Mīnne sluman
nǽfre drēfað eft þā guman."
Ond sē ceorl cwæþ: "Ik ne kare
þæt þei deiden – ill þei ware."
415 þus in tūne ealra tungan
blīðe ond wynlīc lēoð nū sungon:
"Endad is nū, Gode þanc,
fācen, fǽr ond fūl gecanc!"

THE ENDE

Whan hir doom in toun was couthe
390 no man wepte for the youthe.
Bolte sayde "They myght nat the,
by hem that dyede on a tree!"
Buk eek sayde: "The laddes wende
yuilnesse is lyues ende."
395 And the gode techer Lampel
sayde: "Hir doom is a ensample."
Quoth the baker: "Many a cake
yifth at th'eendyng mochel ake".
Ion the gode uncle sede
400 "Yuil doom thurgh yuil dede".
But the oolde fermout thoght
"Al their was sal greue me noght".
Shortly, owher in the toune
herd was glad blisful roune
405 "Free we ben now, bi our othe,
of the malefactours bothe!"

God that rulist elde and youthe
Of the translatour haue routhe;
Eek the poure humble scryue
Ryghtwis on erthe lat hym thryue.
Lat vs with thy swete sone
Al in heuenriche wone;
Close nat the heuen doris
Hard, though iust, on Mak and Morris.

Quhan thir thingis in toun war couth,
Thar wes littill duill nor routh.
Wedo Bautie, mild and saft,
Quod: "I this foirbodit aft!"
405 Tailyour Bukkie: "It is ryff,
Maliss beis na mint off lyff!"
Tharapon said Doctour Lampill:
"Weill be this men tak exampill!"
Maister baiker quod: "Sa beit!
410 Quhairfor is mennis tuthe sa sweit!
Evin guid Eme Fred avowis:
"Luik quhat cummis off evill mowis!"
Bot Makkinla off the Brae
Thocht: "Aw dinna cair ane strae!"
415 And, in beiff, in haill the toun
Gaid ane jocound murmur roun:
"God be thankit! Quha in deid
Off thir raskaillis fand remeid!"

Glossaries

The subsequent glosses are meant to provide the most necessary information on the meanings of words or phrases which have no equivalent in Standard English or whose form is so divergent that the correspondence is difficult to identify. Some readers will find the lists too exhaustive; others will miss some glosses for words whose meanings they cannot deduce from their forms and contexts – these should then be looked up in the dictionaries named in the Introduction. The Old English version would have needed more than 300 glosses; I have refrained from providing them because of their great number but also because of the divergence in Old English grammar, which does not permit a reader to understand the text if he only knows the words. On the other hand, the number of glosses is no safe indication of the difficulty of a text or its distance from Standard English: The number of glosses for the Krio or Middle English texts is lower than many would have thought, but it rises steeply for the rural/traditional Scottish texts and for the N version. Although the number of glosses is a somewhat subjective affair, it may be of interest to rank the subsequent lists according to their length:

G	Glasgow	(47)	X	Middle Scots	(124)
K	Krio	(57)	N	Northumbrian	(143)
M	Middle English	(66)	L	Lallans	(154)
I	N Ireland	(75)	S	Shetland	(171)
J	Jamaican	(75)	A	NE Scots (Aberdeen)	(236)
T	Tok Pisin	(95)	O	Old English	(305)
C	Cameroonian	(105)			

Glossary for Meyk un Moas (Northumbrian)

skeylaak – escapade 3 daa – father 4 saa – adage 5 swaap – exchange, gaiorn – grimace 9 yow – ewe 11 tyul – trouble 12 beyd – stay 13 wheyles – sometimes 16 shaan – shown, nyen – none I 23 canny – pleasant 25 pullits, banties – poultry breeds 27 forbey – besides 29 ey – always, lick – outdo 30 flock – cloth shreds, tick – mattress cover 38 huz – we, fettle – destroy 51 gowp – gulp 52 marras – comrades 55 tin un tuthor gaiyit – this and that way 56 iv i staiyit – in a state 57 lowp – leap 58 'tear and reel, fall over' 61 clamjafrey – riot 65 clishmaclavor – clamorous noise 66 owor-aad – overawed 67 hoy – fling 70 gob – mouth 72 gar – compel 73 glift – frightened 75 aglay – astray 77 hack – cut, dowly – miserable 78 dowf – dull, blunkit – expressionless II 86 heynd – farm-hand 90 eed – eyed 91 ploat – pluck 94 'hairy caterpillar, worm and maggot' 97 neb – nose out 98 speel – climb 99 keek – peer 106 treem – slim 119 teyke – dog 120 theek – thatch, heyke – lift (raised the roof = was very noisy) 125 'startled, choked, distracted, scared' 128 aal foond – food etc. provided 129 fond – foolish, bowdikeyte – rascal 131 bray – thump 135 baiyit – food 136 aiyit – eaten 137 smork – smirk 138 teyme – while, raad – roared III 143 owt – anything 144 naithin, nowt – nothing 145 duds – clothes 146 ganzies – jumpers 147 breeks – trousers 148 caped, cowled – with attached cape, hood 154 cloot – piece of cloth 155 hyuks un een – hooks and eyes 158 'no one offends a fixer's pride' 163 born – stream 165 tyestral – villain 166 dree – dread 169 hwin – furze 172 goniel – rustic fool 173 soe – sew, howk – dig 174 gowk – cuckoo 176 kinda nooled – rather broken-spirited 177 camsteery – wild 178 cf. the proverb "Even the worm can turn" **184** eesel – himself **18** spyate – flood **187** plodge – wade **190** weel spent – much exhausted **191** wark – throbbing pain **193** pressinhorse – tailor's ironing bench **194** speyght – in spite of **196** keyte – stomach **198** gaar – cause **202** 'now we've out-witted them!'

IV   208 fley – smart **216** sair – sorely **218** trick – trump card **224** mense – reputation **238** nigh on fooll – nearly full **239** baccy theak – tobacco thatch **240** 'to trap him without warning' **246** bleezis up – enlivens **257** cowps ees creels – turns over heels **262** bray – dent **263** bittock – little bit **266** Aad Neeck – the Devil

V   283 fettle – condition **284** canny – quite well **290** hippint – affected by muscle-strain **297** sic i bedlim – such a madhouse **298** waam breecks – hot bricks to warm the bed **306** 'earwigs with clawing tails' **314** hwick – teeming with life **326** shaapish – quickly **330** 'throwing insects left and right' **331** stot – bounce **335** tot – drink

VI   340 Pyaist – Pasche **344** yeuky – itchy **345** lang seyn – long since **348** lain – lone **358** cowp – overturn **360** clagged – stuck **362** laand – arrive **364** spyed – sped **371** 'unknown and clandestinely' **375** squeak – escape **376** rede – advice

VII   379 feckliss – valueless **381** poak – sack **386** tweeg – realise **391** misdoot – suspect **396** shutt – chute **397** brust – burst **399** stoowor – dustcloud **402** gissie – pig **404** patcht up – assembled the story **414** gowkish – foolish

Glossary for Mack an Maurice (Northern Ireland)

Firnenst – foreword **2** weeans – children **3** baygles – ill-mannered young people **4** thrahin – wicked behaviour **5** mik their saul – turn their mind to spiritual matters **8** ketthers – badly adjusted people **10** plasthers – inadequates **13** cod – tell lies to, poke – interfere with **14** prog – steal from **16** dibble – make holes for planting potatoes

I   26 a howl – I guarantee **31** dale – there's not **34** skelly – quick look **37** dandher – walk slowly, looking for something **40** farls – soda bread **47** cake – bread **51** gorb – glutton **53** dilseys – foolish creatures **54** banjaxed – caught up **62** scrake – scream of agony **77** kake – peep, growse – sad frown

II   84 stoom – stroke **86** faizant – pleasurable **91** moilly – bald **95** keen – lament the dead **96** gowl – make a noise in the throat **98** bost – flimsy **105** corly cale – cabbage with wrinkled leaves **109** biz ap – were well organized **118** hallion – wicked boy **125** gob – mouth **126** hob – fireside **128** skelp – beat severely, fʌll as shʌkhs – full enough to burst **137** nyʌkt – stolen **139** gʌlpin – greedy boy

III   145 bum-freeze – short **148** damn the hate – there was very little **154** clout – clothes **162** shʌkh – stream **165** glick – sly **167** boxty – saw raggedly **179** culchee – ignorant boy **188** tink – tinker (who would grab anything) **190** sprakhal – struggle (ungainly) **193** thromakh – fix, mess **194** foundther – severe chill **201** pakhal – naughty boy

IV   210 long head – intelligence **213** sizim – wise saying **216** taws – a two-tailed strap **222** shire his head – relax, settle his nerves **228** mass – respect **247** ket-light – very light **255** crooksheen lawn – jug of whisky **259** stoor – dust **263** chullers – cheeks **264** black as toal's coat – extremely black and dirty **265** rib – strand **273** bardicks – possessions **275** bucko – naughty boy

V   295 snood – covering for the head **304** crock – pot **308** dewels – roaches **324** dishabels – night clothes **329** borl – whirl of excitement

VI   337 biz ree – is invariably happy **343** damned as but – as sure as I'm here **349** ark o male – flour container **369** screw – shrewmouse

VII   375 howl yir cup – not so fast **377** sleekid lags – sly boys **397** gossoon – boy.

Glossary for Dod and Davie (Scots, Lallans)

1 Maun – must, thole – suffer **8** gars – makes **13** ploy – amusement **20** waled – chose **21** kent – learned.

I **30** dandy – suitably **34** bide – bear **42** pinkie – little finger **45** skeelie – skilful **48** begoud – began **50** pree – taste **51** eident – diligent **52** dawd – lump **52** warsle – wrestle **55** jinkin – swerving, joukin – dodging, fleggit – frightened, worrit – upset **57** flauchter – flutter **58** collieshangie – uproar **59** fankelt – entangled **60** runkelt – wrinkled **61** craig – neck **62** fear-fangit – panic-stricken, melled – mixed **64** kain – rent in kind **66** yammer – noise **69** een – eyes **71** brawest – most beautiful **73** dool – sorrow **77** douce – grave.

II **84** wycelike – wise **85** umquhile – former **90** scuddie-nakit – naked to the skin **91** pookit – plucked **94** scartit – scratched, stour – dust **95** grat – wept, saut – salt(y) **97** reek – smell **99** lum – chimney **105** ashet – large dish **106** champit – mashed, neeps – turnips **111** unco – extremely **113–117** (onomatopoetic) **121** blate – slow **123** stishie – uproar **124** toddlin ben – ambling in **125** dumfounert – stupefied **129** ill-faured – ugly, gett – bastard **131** skelpit – struck **133** dang – knock.

III **143** shiftin claes – change of clothes after working hours, breeks – trousers **145** cutty – short **146** pokes – pockets **147** bespak – ordered **152** tint – lost, lowss – loose **154** owre ill – too bad **157** chiel – fellow **159** callant – lad **162** blatter – rattling sound **166** smaithers – small bits **169** darg – task **171** geck – mock **181** brod – board **183** yatter – chatter **185** stramash – tumult, boomin – increasing **186** soomin – swimming **191** onie road – anyway, forby – besides, atweel – of course **193** ongauns – events **194** wame – stomach **196** flet-airn – flattening-iron **197** kyte – belly.

IV **206** comprie – understand **207** scrievin – writing **208** gumption – quickness of understanding **214** dominie – teacher **221** moil – drudgery **227** rype – ransack **233** smooled – slipped **242** skail – disperse **243** tid – mood **245** oxtered – took under his arm **247** linkit – walked briskly, canty – lively, crouse – cheerful **250** syne – then **254** gear – household goods, aa roads – in all directions **256** sneeshin-mill – snuff-box **263** neb – nose, lugs – ears **266** powe – head **268** wittan – knowledge, leal – genuine **269** stieve – strong.

V **279** mensefu – courteous **284** spunks – matches, aiblins – perhaps **286** kittlin – tickling **292** fegs! – truly! **294** dram – glass of whisky **296** bield – protect **300** airt – direction **304** bum-cloke – flying beetle **308** shog – shake **314** cutty sark – shirt cut down (cf. Burns' "Tam o' Shanter") **315** steeks – shuts, coories – snuggles **317** press – crowd **318** blouter – burst **322** nesty – nasty **324** lowpit – jumped, gey – very **328** rowth – plenty **330** stramps – stamps on **331** tent – heed.

VI **338** kirk-gaun – church-going, baxter – baker **339** graith – equipment **342** ettle – try **346** sprauchle – scramble **349** clour – bump **357** in a fix – in trouble **358** happit – enveloped, gouie – sticky **360** unco – weird **363** lowin – glowing **366** to a T – perfectly **372** dagont – confounded.

VII **380** humphin – carrying on his back **383** ferlie-full – astonished **383** peched – panted **385** forforn – forlorn **386** dernin – hiding **387** heck – gad **388** shools – shovels, skellums – rascals **394** cowps – overturns **396** stounds – clangs **398** blads – fragments **399** foolies – fowls **400** moolies – crumbs.

E **402** fient – scarcely **412** gomerel – fools **416** blydesome – joyful **417** quat – rid, free.

Glossary for Matt an Malkie (Glasgow)

1 weans – children 8 up thur jouks – covertly, 'up their jerseys' 12 knockin – stealing.

I   terr – amusement 22 cannae whack thum – can't beat them 25 blaw-oot – noisy party 35 howkin – digging up 36 furby – moreover 39 quick as winkie – in a flash 40 piece – sandwich 41 dauds – pieces 66 rammy – fight.

II   92 scuddy – naked 101 lum – chimney 106 ashet – deep plate 107 peas-brose – pease porridge 120 dreep – drop 127 messan – wretched mongrel 134 ablow – below.

III   144 nicky-tams – workmen's trousers 154 keep upsides –ingratiate oneself 159 brig – bridge 166 shirrick – jeer at 180 stank – drain in gutter 184 hudgie – a stolen 'lift' 187 kerry-oan – carry-on 188 gutsache – stomach pains 191 furrit – forward.

IV   225 bags a – plenty of 227 snuck – sneaked 231 tims – empties 260 bauldy-bane – derisive term applied to a bald man.

V   279 giein him gyp – causing him pain 289 baffies – slippers 291 whit aw – all that 298 bumcloack – cockchafer 304 cloacks – insects, cockroaches 308 pixie – pointed (as on a child's hood) 309 rowed – wrapped 324 blooters – smashes.

VI   331 dae a line – do good business 343 stoor – dust 354 jammy-fingered – prone to theft 357 gaun great – going well 361 oot the gemme – hors de combat.

VII   374 humphin – humping 408 gie a doacken – care twopence.

Glossary for Mac an Matthy (Northeastern/Aberdeenshire)

Two general characteristics of the Northeastern dialects are the loss of initial /ð/ in pronouns and adverbs: ey, eir, iss, at, ere (though the standard spelling of the definite article is retained for ease of reading), and the replacement of standard /ʍ /by /f/:fa 'who', fit 'what', fin 'when', far 'where', foo 'how', fite 'white'. Note nae 'no/not'.

2 royit – mischievous, loon(ie) – young boy 3 nickum – rascal 5 douce – gentle, genty – well-mannered 6 wysins – advice, tenty – careful 7 snirt – snigger 8 rede – advice, hidlin – secret, chirt – inward laughter 10 gleg – eager 11 towt – torment, swick – cheat 14 rig – frolic, daffin – fun 16 deece – bench 18 gate – road 19 dool – sorrow.

I   23 steir – trouble 27 nooanan – now and then 28 birsselt – roasted, skirlie pan – frying pan 31 cod – pillow 32 caalrife – cold 34 ava – at all 35 blye – happy 36 paachtie – proud 37 'gud – began 38 gink – trick 39 skeely – smart, bled – blade 40 fang – slice, sned – cut up 41 pickie – piece 42 crannie – little finger 43 wap – tie 45 lair – lay 46 deem – woman 47 ferlie – remarkable thing 52 nirl – morsel 53 preive – try 55 ruggin – pulling 56 fersell – energetic 57 flaffin – fluttering, lift – sky 59 gizzent – withered 62 fleggit – frightened, peeack – cluck, fleitch – beg 63 swythe – quickly 64 or –before 66 yammer – din 68 gastrous – horrifying 74 futtle – knife, fessen – fetched 76 breet – creature.

II   82 cower – recover from, hertscaad – anguish 83 canny – careful 85 weird – fate, harl – drag 86 dreich – dismal 94 chingles – gravel, scart – scratch 95 fegs – truly! grat – wept 97 yoam – smell, nacket – rascal 99 goam – stare, lum – chimney 101 sotter – sizzle 102 skellet – frying pan, fittan braa! – how splendid! 105 ashet – large plate, wale – choose 106 drappie – small quantity, saatit kail

– salted cabbage **107** byous fain – very fond **110** timmerin – activity, mineer – disturbance **119** dowf – stupid **122** speil – climb **125** stookie – plaster statue **129** gutsy – greedy, tyke – cur **130** pyke – beat **133** gyte –mad **134** wyte – fault **136** hoven – swollen, snocher – snore **57** rossen – roasted.

III **143** ouk – week **144** quyte – coat, bouk – body **145** queetikins – gaiters, moggan – footless stocking **147** trig – neat **149** sort – repair **150** duds – clothes, cloot – patch **151** tint – lost **156** darg – work **157** eident – industrious, chiel – fellow **161** door-steen – doorstep **162** burn – small river **162** creen – murmur **163** buird – plank, lig – lie **167** sweirt – reluctant **169** sinner – divide **170** lant – jeer **173** thole – tolerate **175** jaa – insult, dree – endure **176** tirravee – passion **177** ellwann – measuring stick, cleek – snatch **178** swippert – quickly, door-cheek – door-post **183** bedeen – at once **187** reefu – panic-stricken **188** claucht – clutch **191** ugsome – hideous **194** wyme – stomach, strait – cramp **196** reese – praise **197** scaam – heat **198** sain – cure, sair – pain **199** crack – conversation.

IV **204** leir – learning **205** A-B brod – alphabet board **206** snod – well-off, bien – comfortable **208** mense – wisdom **209** traachle – labour **210** man – must **211** smeddum – common-sense, resourcefulness **212** tent – attend to **214** squeel – school **218** dominie – teacher **219** lack – defect **220** mangin – craving **221** threep – insist **226** chaa – prank **227** gowk – fool, gype – trick **230** leal – faithful, stainch – dependable **231** list – wish **232** fussle-kist – pipe organ **233** smool – sneak **234** geeties – brats **239** wap – shake **241** snoove – slink, trou – believe **242** skail – empty **244** steek – shut **245** stent – task **248** canty – cheerful **249** rype – rake out **250** lunt – light **253** smiddrins – fragments, dung – smashed **254** belter – heavy blow, bung – crash, bang **256** trackie – teapot **257** throu'der – mixed up **258** fuff – explode **265** scowdert – scorched **266** flaacht – wisp **268** souch – sound **272** crockanition – fragments.

V **277** clachan – village **282** sair – serve **284** lunt – match **285** thraa – twist, rack – sprain **288** stang – pain **289** sneesh – snuff, pree – taste **291** seel – blessings **292** machts – health **294** bachles – slippers **295** hoose-quyte – dressing-gown, hoomet – night-cap **295** stairve – freeze **300** bar – fun **301** jalouse – guess, bam – prank **303** hiz – us **304** goloch – beetle **307** chaav'n – working **309** pyockie – bag **310** bockie – frightful creature **311** queetin – quilt **313** coorie – snuggle **314** toorie – tassel **317** scart – scratch **318** clock – beetle **321** gowl – yell **322** skeer – fearful thing **326** sclim – climb **328** birl – whirl, bum – buzz **329** fleysome – fearful **330** dunt – thump, dird – wallop.

VI **337** Pace – Easter **339** crumpy – crisp **342** cheerie pyke – tasty snack **343** sleekit – cunning **349** mael-kist – meal chest **351** skypel – rascal **352** doo – pigeon **353** reck – care **355** creepie – stool **357** sosst – messed **360** sclatched – plastered **362** benk – bench **363** een – oven, quile – coal, a-lowe – flaming **364** howe – hollow **367** by wi't – dead (euphemism) **370** ramsh – munch.

VII **377** haggie — gash **380** bere – barley **384** dag – dashed **387** sheel – shovel **398** nirlie – fragment **399** gollop – gobble **400** jeukie – duck **411** begeck – trick.

Glossary for Jarm an Jeemsie (Shetland)

Reebald – scoundrel **4** oolet – brat **5** lear – learning **6** leet – heed **7** skirl – shriek **8** smeeg – smirk **9** aaber – eager **11** hatter – harass, ledder – thrash, baess – cattle **12** raander – pilfer **13** maddrim – fun **14** lichtsome – cheerful **17** less a less – alas, tweetishee – a malediction **19** vyld – vile **20** tö-tak – disreputable character.

I **31** stirn – shiver **34** dree – endure **39** scad – hurry **40** cassen – beginning to decay, minkie – small **45** smoot – slink **46** peerie wyes – cautiously **48** rex – stretch, hass – throat **52** glaep – gulp, kwilk – swallow, wack – share **54** ill-helt – expression of annoyance **55** pin – move swiftly **56** nyigg – tug **60** keek – peer **62** gluffed – scared **66** reel – commotion, splore – turmoil **67** spunder – rush **74** tully – large knife **75** krang – carcase **77** dumpeesed – depressed, croose – cheerful.

II **82** lay – mood **86** soch – sigh, blate – timid **87** swack – energetic **88** dastreen – last night **89** gret – wept **90** whet – stop **94** scobbins – pan-scrapings **95** gowl – weep loudly **97** waff – odour **99** glinder – peer **100** scrime – observe with difficulty **101** gözren – gizzard **103** truncher – large plate **105** coarn – small quantity **108** kirsen – decent **110** trang – very busy **112** eence a errant – for that purpose **120** yalk – yelp **122** proil – spoil, löf – palm of the hand **123** hubbleskyoo – uproar **129** condwined – hateful **130** swee – smart **133** oob – moan **136** grice – pig(s), skroo – stack of corn **137** footh – large quantity.

III **143** plags – garments, strood – suit of clothes **144** ooen – woollen **146** wirset – woolen, mutch – woman's cap **147** scam – blemish **149** stret – tight fitting **150** spret – burst **151** sark – shirt **153** sklent – rent **154** ent – heed **156** leid – diligence **160** nyagg – ache **166** filska – high-spirited fun **169** clooky – tricky **171** aalie lamb – lamb reared at home **173** skyimp – ironic praise **174** löd – mood, jee – move **177** bismar – wooden beam, nev – fist **179** barm – seethe with rage **180** gölbröl – bellow **181** sprit – run fast **185** spricklin – floundering **187** rip – current **188** pipper – tremble **194** bool cramp – colic **198** helly – weekend.

IV **208** cuggly – shaky **216** sheeld – fellow **218** ant – heed **255** owresteer – rumbustious **231** prunk – well-poised **232** runk – play with gusto **233** hint inby – steal indoors **247** stend – walk with long strides, but-end – kitchen cum living-room **252** nyarg – nagging person, nyitter – complaining person **253** laid in coom – smashed **254** oondömious – enormous **255** lem – crockery **260** ava – at all **261** dwaam – a faint **264** shaela – dark grey, oo – wool **265** collcoomed – burned to a cinder, tiv – tuft **266** ill trift – a mild oath **269** varg – work messily **270** döless – indolent, sharg – nag **272** nyook – corner.

V **284** pantin – wooden-soled slipper **285** yucky – itchy **287** oy – nephew **288** cloor – scratch **294** rivlins – hide shoes **304** hundiclock – large beetle **305** voar – spring **306** oag – crawl **307** filsket – frisky **308** shiggle – shake **310** mitten – grasp **311** med – made **316** coonterpeen – bedcover **318** yasp – lively **322** ill-laek – ugly, yock – grasp **324** spang – leap **327** mird – swarm **328** arl – crawl **329** frush – splutter with rage **332** scart – scratch.

VI **339** leelang – livelong **340** curny – fruity **346** reesle – struggle noisily **349** scunner – disgust(ing person), salist – pause **351** trivle – grope **355** ging in soe – fall to pieces **357** clatched – besmeared **361** forsmo – snub **371** ree – squeal, gorie – exclamation of surprise.

VII **375** tak vaar – take heed **377** spölli – spoil **380** bere – barley **382** doontöm – downpour **384** dwine – confound **388** headicraa – head-over-heels **391** heest dee – hurry up **393** reck – reach **395** snyirk – creak, clump – make a heavy noise **398** skroil – fragment **407** lö – listen **410** siccar – fierce **414** soar a peel – Devil a scrap, työr – care **416** odious – extremely.

Glossary for Max an Marris (Jamaican Creole)

Rude – precociously insolent, bway – boy(s), weh – which, who; **1** pickney – child(ren) **3** suo-so – only **6** fiesty – impudent **8** Jeyes – an old-fashioned antiseptic **9** coke-nat – coconut, saafa – softer **10** dread – youth with Rastafarian affiliation; delinquent **11** was'e – waste **13** ignarance – folly, rudeness, anger **14** mango-time – period during which mango harvest is gathered **20** sipple – slippery, koo – look at!

I **23** mine – to care for **27** friggisee – fricassee **35** en – hens **40** lickle – little **41** jine – join **42** nancy-web – spider web **51** nyam – devour greedily **57** flatta – flutter **67** kuol-sweat – cold sweat **69** Lawd-a-massy – Lord have mercy! puor me gal – me poor girl! **71** eye-waata – tears **80** faya-stick –live coal, burning brand.

II **91** memba – remember **100** tuos – toast **101** kyaan don – beyond expectation **103** skellion – variety of onion, dutch-pat – deep iron skillet **109** pickle-backle – jar in which pickled peppers are stored **111** lang-ead – cunning **118** poppop – folk name for a pet dog **121** siem – same, een – in **123** eena – into, saal – salt **126** gaan – away **128** a mus – it must be, fi-yuh – your **129** gwine – going to.

III **143** drodgin clothes – working clothes **150** piecen – lengthen **158** seh – says **159** ginnal – trickster **163** weh – where, a fi pass – has to pass over **170** laughin kya-kya – laugh loudly, in a vulgar way **171** cho – common exclamation expressing contempt **177** paan – seize in hand **182** lick – hit, strike **186** kaaf – cough(ing) **190** sief-sief – safely **198** guol – gold.

IV **209** higle – idle, smaddy – somebody, person **217** sieka dat – because of that **220** jackass-caan – a type of coarse tobacco **223** nize – noise, badaration – botheration **227** uova-sweet – give great pleasure **233** aagan – organ **249** siddong – sits down **256** pre-pre – splinters, scraps.

V **285** was'-sting – wasp sting **327** temparated – angry **328** grong – ground.

VI **337** bullah kiek – a sweet soda bread **346** jang-crow – the john crow, turkey buzzard **368** abeng – conch horn.

VII **380** hais – hoist **382** 'tep – step.

As with the preceding J and the subsequent T versions, glossaries for K and C are problematic for readers who do not have an elementary knowledge of the language. Although some 80–90% of the Krio and CamP vocabularies can be traced to English, most words have been modified phonologically and semantically (which can include a shift of part of speech). The phonological differences are mainly due to the facts that

a) Krio and CamP have a smaller phonemic inventory; vowel length is not phonemic.

b) Consonant clusters, especially at the beginning and end of words, tend to be avoided (more so in Krio than in CamP; also cf. C and T): *story* = tori C1, stori K; *strong* = trɔng C9, tranga K62; *stick* = stik C112, tik 'tree' K304; *stand* = stan C127, tan K7; *stretch* = trech C319.

c) CamP speakers frequently devoice /b,d,g/ in wordfinal position (cf. T): bik 'big'.

Some knowledge of English:Krio and English:CamP sound correspondences will greatly facilitate the identification of etymological equivalences. Specimens illustrating such difficulties – and the effect of phonological mergers – can be found in such rhyme pairs as:

Krio: *fowl:all* (23f.), *warm:come* (31f.), *first:ghost* (63f.), *pipe:help* (235f.), *short:mouth* (415f.);

CamP: *get:bird* (23f.), *egg:take* (25f.), *house:lost* (77f.), *rest:place* (165f.), *church:house* (233f.), *burst:torch* (245f.), *bad:part* (307f.).

Glossary for Maks ɛn Mɔris (Krio)

Bɔbɔ – boys **2** yɛri – hear, pikin – children **5** kɔmɔt na waf – 'come from the wharf' = are vagrants, and hence ill-mannered **7** tan – are **12** bɛlful – thoroughly **14** saful – quiet, shek – shake, fɔm – give trouble.

I   **48** tret – stretch out **58** wahala – woe, ful mɔt –is too shocking for words **60** ling – is slanting **62** ala – cries **63** bay fos – involuntarily **72** dunya – world **78** fing – nothing.

II   **96** timap – stood **98** ɔjɛnt – urgent **106** shapka – fruit of the sorrel plant, usually cooked in palm oil, lili – little **110** awuf – free food **128** fɔdɔm – fell **130** andul – punish.

III   **148** chɛr – torn **151** usay – where, wesmata – whatever the matter **159** ambɔgin – harass **163** pantap – on top **171** Bɔskot – Tattercoat **174** fityay – insults **176** sote – until, wan bɔs – nearly burst **178** domɔt – entrance **192** at – hurt.

IV   **214** sabi – expertise **221** yagba – hard work **227** bren – brain **236** ɛp – help **267** udat – who **272** pwɛl – destroyed.

V   **281** do klin – morning **288** bifo jɛk – in no time **290** nɔf – a lot **303** gɔngrɔbi – bumble-bee **316** slip fɔ am – slept in peace **319** dos – bite **322** ɛlɛya – pests.

VI   **350** kyas – cask **369** arata – rats **370** cham – chewed up **372** yanda – yonder.

VII   **376** kɔp go ful – will meet your doom **394** ma – without doubt **406** 'You understand, don't you, that these two are ill-mannered' **410** bigyay – greedy **412** tan – results.

Glossary for Tar an Tava (Cameroon Pidgin)

4 fain palava – look for mischief **8** hambak – annoy **9** trɔng-hɛd – stubborn **11** bɛnbɛn – go wrong **13** naknak – hit repeatedly, bif – animals **16** sidɔng – stay **17** helele – o dear! **19** wuna – you (pl.), kɔni – trick(s) **21** buk – writing.

I   **25** fɔsika – because **27** gri – agree **29** hapi taim – times of celebration **31** agɛn – in addition **32** skin – body **36** i gɛt agɛn – also **41** njanga – finger-sized crayfish **42** mek nyanga – be very proud of oneself **44** fɔ ɛni sai – all sides **46** kampɔng – yard **47** wan time – immediately **50** fain – look for **57** wandaful – amazing, strange **60** pas mak – exceedingly **61** hala – cry **63** pala – room, not the kitchen **67** wei – exclamation of horror **68** ashia – empathy formula **69** swit mi – gave me joy **77** sɔfri, sɔfri – softly, quietly **78** dong lɔs – was deprived of.

II   **81** kraidai – wake, mourning period **83** mɛmba sei – decided that **84** smɔl – young **87** na dai – excessively **88** luk di bɛt fɔ ai – looked closely at the birds **99** mbanda – roof, rafters **100** wanda – delight **101** langa – desire for food **105** njamanjama – green vegetable like spinach **110** sotei – again and again **111** lɔng hed – inventive **116** tot – pull up **118** wikɔp – get up **119** wandaz – exclamation of joy and amazement **131** mɔta stik – mortar for pounding fufu **133** fɔ ɔp – towards heaven.

III   **143** bos – boast **145** pɛnsɛl fut – narrow legs **147** danshiki – local shirt **148** abada –long, embroidered coat for men **149** lapa – local shirt, buba – blouse **151** palava – problem **152** bɔs – torn **154** lassai – bottom **162** tumtum – roar **164** hamak – hammock **168** mindru – middle, hia hɔt – suffer **172** wowo – very ugly **184** chakara – break into bits **196** 'Everything depends on her inventiveness'.

IV   **203** panapu – parable, wise saying **205** daso – only **207** ɔl sɛns – all wisdom, tali – count **208** chinda – elders, Bali – centre for Baptist education **211** katakis –catechist **215** sɔf laik san – as elusive as quicksilver **224** ɛnjoi i skin – relax **231** gegeru – stringed instrument **232** sing – singing and music **240** hawe – as **247** Tata – God **258** bebi-dɔl – rag-doll **260** ninga – slave **261** drai – bald **265** tonton – excuse **267** chɔp Pa Mat i chia – replace Pa Mat **271** kul hat – consoles.

V   278 shidɔng – live **279** fɔ i kɔna – near him **291** put snɔf – inhale snuff **306** krɔkrɔ – skin disease **309** kwa –local bag **311** trɔng-ai – bold, brazen **319** lidaman – leader **329** bris – wind **330** hɔha – creepy-crawly.

VI   339 chɔp-haus man – hotel proprietor, baker **341** 'cassava delicacy, fritters' **342** kɔki kɔn – corn delicacy **348** kenja – raffia basket in which birds are kept, often hung from the ceiling **352** baf – white, starched trousers **358** Babanki Ston – outcrop of stones in Bamenda, landmark **366** bagɛt – French-type loaves.

VII   377 sɛka wɛti – why, bruta – brothers **378** makuta – sack **379** tot – carry **381** i wan go – as he went along.

Glossary for Max na Moritz (Tok Pisin)

In the case of Tok Pisin it is especially difficult to know which words ought to be glossed. Most words derive from English but they have been modified phonologically, syntactically and semantically, and so it is often difficult to spot correspondences. The difficulties have been increased for readers familiar with the orthography of Standard English because TP's orthography is essentially phonemic; this means that correspondences such as *tikap, spun* (255) = 'teacup, spoon' which would otherwise be apparent are hidden. The following rules will help the reader:

Fricatives are usually represented by stops, which are devoiced at the end of words; initial and end clusters are variably reduced; all sibilants are **s**; some vowel contrasts are lost (long vs. short, **a** vs. **e**); there is no postvocalic **r** (as in present-day RP). This means that the following words are quite regular reflexes of their English cognates: **40** *tret* – thread, **82** *pilim* – feel, **126** *plua* – floor, **165** *bris* – bridge, **190** *sua* – shore, **259** *klaut* – cloud, **276** *tanim pes* – turn the page, **370** *tit* – teeth, tooth **391** *pren* – friend. *pen* is both 'pain' and 'pen'; *bek* both 'bag' and 'back'; *pes* both 'page' and 'face'. Where such correspondences are more or less obvious in the context, words have not been glossed – but I have glossed cases such as *aninit* 'underneath', *senisim* 'change' and *suim* 'chew'.

Manki – boy, Siaman – German, tanim – translate. **1** pasin – manner, behaviour, olsem – thus, like, as **3** kranki – odd, wrong **8** lap – laugh **9** tok bilas – insult **16** bladiful – bloody fool **17** tasol – only, but **20** ating – possibly.

I   23 hap – side, direction **24** kakaruk – domestic fowl **26** pisin – bird **27** kiau – egg **29** as – cause, source **30** kaikai – eat **33** meri – woman **38** kirapim – start **40** pasim – fasten **54** brata – brother, friend **58** tarangu! – oh dear! **60** diwai – tree **64** dai – death **65** lapun – old **72** blu – unlucky **73** belhevi – sad.

II   90 skin nating – naked **107** kabis – cabbage **108** rabis – rubbish **111** paslain – before **112** pislain –string, fishing-line **113** haisimap – hoist up **126** sanap – stand up **137** slek – slack.

III   145 samapim – sew **159** kos – course **161** baret – ditch, drain **162** poret – front **166** apinun – evening **171** blakbokis – fruit-bat **187** pekato – sin **188** pato –duck **198f.** ain(imaut) – (to) iron.

IV   209 gavman – government **215** les – lazy **217** lesbaga – lazy person, yesa – agree **222** brus – local tobacco **224** kisim win – take a rest **225** kru – brain **226** bagar(im)apim – spoil **252** malolo – rest **263** Buka – island in the N. Solomon province of PNG whose inhabitants (also called Buka) are renowned for their extreme blackness **264** kela – bald, kuka – crab **269** standet ten – tenth grade in school **271** spak –intoxication.

V 280 kandere – mother's brother **283** buai – areca nut, chewed with daka (betel-pepper) and kambang (lime) for its stimulant effect **284** laka – is it not so? **285** natnat – mosquito, kaikaim – bite **287** kus – mucus **291** spak – drunk, tudak – night **300** belgut – well disposed **301** mismis – kin **303** binatang – insect **304** korakum – tree ant, lang – a fly **307** meknaisim – shake **312** ananit – underneath **319** musmus – bedbug.

VI 337 pati – celebration **348** kotkot – crow **350** senisim – change **354** bet – shelf **356** poris – porridge **357** do –dough (ol i kolim 'called' introduces new words in TP) **369** sel – shell **370** suim – chew.

VII 380 sol – shoulder, glasim – stare at **392** wilwilim –grind **401** Post-Courier – the principal newspaper in Papua New Guinea **402** seksek – shake, guria – tremble **403** autim – utter **406** giaman – trickery **412** longlong – crazy **413** kas – cards **414** gau ta lasi! – it is nothing! (in Hiri Motu, another widespread lingua franca in Papua New Guinea).

Glossary for Mak and Morris (Middle English)

2 bale – harm **6** wile – guile, subtlety, bare the flour – excelled **8** weird – fate **9** steuen – voice **12** day – damned **13** lither – wicked **14** derne – secretly **15** deres – animals **21** layne – deny **22** almayne – Germany.

I 26 volatyles – birds **27** eyren – eggs **32** queme – cosy **35** meynee – household **41** gynne – deceit **63** bour – chamber **74** yfere – together **78** leste – like.

II 81 wende – thought **86** deyntee – delicious **88** 'May they, then, rest in my paunch!' **91** hulde – plucked **97** brede – roast **98** yede – went **118** schille – shrill **131** smerte – painfully **134** claght – caught **136** Cokayne – the land of plenty **140** fit – story, section.

III 145 jupes – jackets, habergeounes – sleeveless coats **153** blyue – quickly **168** hokreden – mocked **172** leel – honest **174** clawe on the galle – scratch a sore spot **175** wood – angry **184** raughte – reached **185** shanke – leg **187** of dawe – to death **193** dighte – applied **195** goos – smoothing iron **196** pose – cold in the head, quakke – frog in one's throat.

IV 206 endite – compose **216** fille – something worthless **218** wede – plant, weed **221** swynkyng – toil **232** wonynge – dwelling **241** quaire – book **248** maumets – heathen idols (or scarecrows) **253** stynte – ended **256** bloman – blackamoor **266** werth – becomes **267** blynne – stop.

V 277 yare – ready **279** fnese – sneeze **288** eme – uncle **314** wlatsom – ugly **316** thede – people.
VI 327 wastelbrede – fine white bread **329** wilnede – desired.
VII 373f. 'Holy cross! Much wheat is running from my sack'. **381f.** 'Dear miller, grind at once these two boys, skin and bones!' **384** bidene – together.
VIII 391 thee – thrive.

For a full commentary see my edition *The gestes of Mak and Morris* (Heidelberg: Winter, 1981).

Glossary for Mak and Moreis (Middle Scots)

Loun – rascal **2** bruitt – report **7** flyte – scoff **9** glaikis – tricks **10** buskit – prepared, smaikis – rascals **13** boun – bound to **15** lout – sit down **16** bink – bench.

I   41 loppis – pieces cut off **42** pink – little finger **44** out on ane ling – at the end of a line **51** blate – shy **56** airt – direction **61** thrappillis – throats , blinnit – stopped **64** swyth – quickly **70** dawtit – pampered **74** gullie – large kitchen knife **80** scape – a turn that a story takes.

II   82 dicht – wiped **87** mensk – honour **93** umquhyll – erstwhile **95** greitis – weeps **101** dispuilyit – robbed **102** ingill – fire, bruilyit – broiled **103** laich hous – cellar, assit – plate **106** wail – choose **108** hett ouir agane – warmed up **119** grouff – rude **123** stour – battle **125** stound – stunned **126** towme – empty **129** poultroun – cowardly villain **130** limmar –villainous **138** kithe – be disclosed.

III   141 fremmit – unknown **143** oukda – weekday **144** trewis – trousers **145** cravattis – shawls **146** justicotis – short, close-fitting coats **147** habuilyiment – clothing **150** gair – enlarge **160** ettillit – endeavoured **162** rais – strong current **164** quhairatour – over which **166** hidlingis – secretly **177** tyt – quickly **178** land – house **188** cleikis – catches **191** mairatour – moreover, als thairanent – as concerning this **193** hentis – gets **194** warkand – aching.

IV   203 ouralquhare – everywhere **222** darg –day's work **226** mynt – aim at **228** in dernë – in secret **232** pibroch – bagpipe music **233** on braid – out of the house **234** peip – peep **242** skaill – disperse **248** cayris – returns, couthie – cosy **249** bigane – begone **254** brall – brawl **256** buist – box **257** elbok chayr – armchair **258** flagratis – bursts out **262** chaffar – wares, coft – bought **268** cairnis – stone piles set up as landmarks **270** lade – load **272** bituik – betook (itself to eternity) **274** outtane – except.

V   282 pay – satisfy **284** spyle – kindling stick **286** yuik – itch, thwak – knock **287** ythand – eager **289** Heland sneischan – Highland snuff **290** neise –sneeze, onleischan – unleashing **291** but byde – without delay **295** mutch – nightcap, muilis – slippers **306** sklent – move sideways, skliddir – slide **308** schoggillis – shake **313** buskit – fitted out **316** cummyr – sorrow **323** scunnyr – disgust **324** leittacamp – bed **326** cuit – ankle, hurdies – buttocks **329** beit – overcome **331** bikkir – struggle **334** redd – rid.

VI   338 fasch – take trouble to **340** gustie – tasty **341** grein – desire **346** peth – path, steep descent, preiff – try **348** devaillis – descends **354** succurit – sugared **356** parrage – porridge **360** feris – companions **363** oyne – oven.

VII   375 dre your weird – suffer your destiny! **376** eird – earth **377** frekkis – bold fellows **379** keltyr – condition (or: coarse grey cloth) **380** turssis – carry as a burden, meltyr – melder **381** warpis – turns slowly **382** girnall – container for grain **384** (Aberdeenshire dialect) 'God! What makes this stuff light?' **387** schulis – shovels **389** schill – chilly **398** mappamound – (in the manner of a) map of the world.

End   406 mint – purpose **412** mowis – jokes.

Bibliography of English translations of *Max und Moritz*

I Standard English

1   1871, by Charles T. Brooks. *Max and Maurice. A Juvenile History in Seven Tricks*. New York: Roberts, 1871-; re-ed. (as *Max and Moritz*) by H. Arthur Klein, New York: Dover, 1962.
Ah, how oft we read or hear of
boys we almost stand in fear of!

2   1874, anonymous. *Max and Moritz, or: The Mischief-Making ... By the Author of "Merry Thoughts"*. London: Mowbray House, 1897 = *Max and Moritz. A Story in Seven Tricks*. München: Braun & Schneider/London: Myers, 1925–59. Revised by Christopher Morley ("Illustrated by Jay"), New York: William Morrow, 1932.
We often must! 'tis sad indeed,
of naughty children hear and read!

3   1914, by Arundell Esdaile. *Max and Moritz ... freely translated*. London: G. Routledge, 1914.
How many dreadful stories we have to hear and read
all about naughty children: it's very sad indeed!

4   1961, by Walter Roome. *Max & Maurice, the story of two rascals in seven pranks*. Montreal: Mansfield Book Mart, 1961; München: Braun & Schneider, 1963.
Oh, what do we hear and read
often of a wicked breed

5   1962, by H. Arthur Klein (Prologue only), in: *Max and Moritz ...* New York: Dover, 1962 (cf. 1).
How often must one read or hear
of children, who should be so dear,

6   1974, by Karl E. Dietrich. *Max and Moritz*. Freiburg im Breisgau: Schillinger, 1974.
How distasteful is the reading
about children of ill breeding!

7   1974, by Karl Schmidt. *Max and Maurice. A story of two mischievous boys in seven tricks*. Klagenfurt: Heyn, 1974,²1980.
Of naughty boys to hear or read
is often very sad indeed.

8   1975, by Anthea Bell. *Max and Moritz. A moral tale*. London: Abelard-Schuman, 1975; herausgegeben und mit Vokabular versehen, München/Wien: Franz Schneider, 1976.
This is the tale of Max and Moritz
and those who wish to read their stories

9   1977, by Rudolf J. Wiemann. *Max and Morry. A story of two boys who play seven tricks*. Manuscript 1977, revised 1982.
Dear, the things one all the time
hears or reads of kids in crime!

10   1979, by Walter W. Arndt. *Max and Moritz*. in his *The Genius of Wilhelm Busch*. Berkeley: California UP, 1982: 25–35; repr. in *Max und Moritz polyglott*. München: dtv, 1982.
Ah, the wickedness one sees
or is told of such as these,

11   1981, by Elly Miller. *Mac and Murray. A Tale of Two Rascals in Seven Episodes* (in this volume);
     separate edition in preparation for Southside, Edinburgh.
     Think how frequently one reads
     of some youngsters' wicked deeds.

11a 1983, by Robert S. Swann. *Max and Maurice. A Story of Two Boys and Their Seven Tricks.*
     Often boys can be precocious
     but some of them are quite atrocious.

II   English and Scottish dialects

12   NORTHUMBRIAN, 1982, by Roland Bibby. *Meyk an Moas. A tyale o twee bad lads an thor*
     sivvin skeylaaks, telt iv aad-fashint Mid-Northumbrian varse by R.B. (in this volume).
     Ee, sic tyales – nee ward uv a lee!
     Tyales o baiorns thit's wickid, hwee,

13   NORTHERN IRELAND, 1981, by A. N. Seymour and Loreto Todd. *Mack an Maurice. A*
     Shannakh for Childher in Seven Cracks torned intil Irish be A.N.S. and L.T. (in this volume).
     We've heard tell or seen it writ
     o weeans that nivir diz their bit,

14   SCOTS, GLASGOW, 1981, by Stephen Mulrine. *Matt an Malkie. A story aboot two boays in*
     sivven terrs translaitit intae Glesga dialeck bi S.M. (in this volume).
     Haw, the wickit things weans dae,
     ye read ur hear aboot, lik say

15   SCOTS, LALLANS, 1981, by J. K. Annand. *Dod and Davie. A tale o twa laddies in seiven*
     ploys owreset intil Scots be J.K.A. (in this volume); separate edition in preparation for Southside,
     Edinburgh.
     What for maun we thole wee laddies
     when they are sic awfu baddies!

16   SCOTS, NORTHEASTERN, 1980–82, by J. Derrick McClure. *Mac an Matthy. A speil aboot*
     twaa royit loonies in seiven pliskies (in this volume).
     Losh! Foo aft we hears or reads
     tales a royit loonies' deeds!

17   SCOTS, SHETLAND, 1982, by Derick Herning. *Jarm an Jeemsie. A tale o twa reebalds in*
     seevin pairts owreset til Shetlandic bi D.H. (in this volume); also separately published by The
     Shetland Times, Lerwick, 1984. ISBN 0-900662-42-5.
     Nooadays der mony boys
     taen till fir der weekit ploys!

III   Pidgins and creoles

18   CAMEROON PIDGIN, 1981, by Loreto Todd. *Tar an Tava. Pikin i tori wei i gɛt sɛvɛn*
     pat, L.T. bin putam fɔ pijin (in this volume).
     A! Di tori dɛm di tɔk
     fɔ pikin wei du bad wɔk.

19   JAMAICAN CREOLE, 1982, by Jean d'Costa. *Max an Marris, two rude bway, seven diffrant badness weh dem do* (in this volume).

Lissen now, som pickney bad:

Two bway rude so tell dem mad!

20   KRIO, 1981–82, by Freddie Jones. *Maks ɛn Mɔris. Stori bɔt tu raskɛl bɔbɔ pan sɛvin trik, na Frɛdi Jons translet am to Krio vas* (in this volume).

A, wi kin rid plɛnti tin

ɔ yɛri bɔt bad pikin!

21   TOK PISIN, 1979, by Don Laycock. *Max na Moritz, stori bilong tupela manki. Wilhelm Busch i bin raitim long tok Siaman, D.L. i bin tanim long tok Pisin* (in this volume).

Pasin bilong manki i olsem:

long olkain trik i no ken sem.

IV Historical versions

22   OLD ENGLISH, 1977, by Manfred Görlach. *Maccus and Mauris. Largiedd on seofon fyttum.* Heidelberg: privately printed 1977; first annotated English edition, Binghamton, N.Y.: CEMERS, 1979.

Hwæt! we gefrugnon fela misdæda

fyrenfremmendra. Fela sceal gebidan

23   OLD ENGLISH, 1983, by Manfred Görlach. *Mac ond Mauris, manwyrhtena wohsong on seofon fyttum* (in this volume).

Hwæt! We hyraþ oft of cildum

ungehyrsumum ond wildum!

24   MIDDLE ENGLISH, 1981, by Manfred Görlach. *The gestes of Mak and Morris.* Heidelberg: Winter, 1981 (repr. in this volume).

Listneth lordes to my tale

how two boyes come to bale!

25   MIDDLE SCOTS, 1984, by Hans H. Meier. *Mak and Moreis. Ane lounis taill disponit in til sevin japis beand heireftir versit in Scottis toung* (in this volume).

A! Quhow comounlie men lernis

Bruitt or taill off cursit bairnis!

Addresses of translators

J. K. Annand
10 House o Hill Row
Edinburgh EH4 2AW
SCOTLAND

Roland Bibby
Westgate House
Dogger Bank
Morpeth
Northumberland
ENGLAND NE61 1RF

Jean d'Costa
RDI Box 2
111 Campus Road
Clinton, N. Y. 13323, USA
(Dept. of English
Hamilton College
Clinton, N.Y.)

Manfred Görlach
Bertolt-Brecht-Str. 116
D-5042 Erftstadt-Liblar
(Universität zu Köln
Englisches Seminar
Albertus-Magnus-Platz
D-5000 Köln 41)

Derick Herning
2, Hayfield Court
Lerwick, Shetland
SCOTLAND

Freddie Jones
Allgemeine Linguistik TU Berlin
Ernst-Reuter-Platz 8
D-1000 Berlin 10
(Dept. of English
Fourah Bay College
Univ. of Sierra Leone
SIERRA LEONE)

Don Laycock
Dept. of Linguistics
Pacific Studies
The Australian National University
G.P.O. Box 4,
Canberra A.C.T. 2601
AUSTRALIA

J. Derrick McClure
4 Rosehill Terrace
Aberdeen AB2 2LF
(Dept. of English, King's College,
Univ. of Aberdeen, Old Aberdeen AB9 2UB)
SCOTLAND

Hans H. Meier
Breitenaustr. 130
CH-8200 Schaffhausen

Elly Miller
20 Marryat Road
Wimbledon Common
London SW19
ENGLAND

Stephen Mulrine
132 Kingswood Drive
Glasgow G44 4RB
SCOTLAND

A.N. Seymour
22 Shanreagh Park
Limavady, co. Derry
N. IRELAND

Loreto Todd
12, Castle Grove Drive
Moor Road
Leeds LS6 4BR
ENGLAND
(School of English
Univ. of Leeds
Leeds LS2 9JT)

WILHELM BUSCH

MAX UND MORITZ

*Eine Bubengeschichte
in sieben Streichen*

In deutschen Dialekten,
Mittelhochdeutsch und Jiddisch
*herausgegeben, eingeleitet und mit
einer Bibliographie versehen
von*

Manfred Görlach

*1982. 178 Seiten mit Abbildungen, Fotos und Karten.
Format 24 x 17 cm. Leinen.*
Empf. Preis DM 24,80
ISBN 3-87118-522-1

Zwei 90er-Kassetten mit acht Parallelversionen:

*Kölsch / Badisch-Pfälzisch / Elsässisch / Züritüütsch / Schwäbisch /
Bairisch / Fränkisch / Schlesisch*
Laufzeit 162 Minuten. Empf. Preis DM 48,—
ISBN 3-87118-530-2

HELMUT BUSKE VERLAG HAMBURG

WILHELM BUSCH

MAX UND MORITZ

In deutschen Dialekten,
Mittelhochdeutsch und Jiddisch

INHALT

   * Die acht Versionen liegen vollständig auf zwei 90er-Kassetten vor. Die Übersetzer sprechen ihre Nachdichtungen, die Version Hägnis wird von seiner Tochter gelesen. Laufzeit 162 Minuten. ISBN 3-87118-530-2